APPLICATIONS
OF THE
ELECTROMAGNETIC
RECIPROCITY PRINCIPLE

by

G. D. MONTEATH

Research Department,
British Broadcasting Corporation,
Kingswood Warren,
Tadworth, Surrey

PERGAMON PRESS

OXFORD · NEW YORK · TORONTO
SYDNEY · BRAUNSCHWEIG

Pergamon Press Ltd., Headington Hill Hall, Oxford

Pergamon Press Inc., Maxwell House, Fairview Park, Elmsford,
New York 10523

Pergamon of Canada Ltd., 207 Queen's Quay West, Toronto 1

Pergamon Press (Aust.) Pty. Ltd., 19a Boundary Street,
Rushcutters Bay, N.S.W. 2011, Australia

Vieweg & Sohn GmbH, Burgplatz 1, Braunschweig

First edition 1973

Library of Congress Catalog Card No. 72-87528

Printed in Germany

08 016895 7

CONTENTS

v

Contents

PREFACE

THIS monograph sets out to show the power of reciprocity as an aid to the theoretical solution of practical problems. A fair proportion of the subject-matter stemmed from my own work in the Research Department of the British Broadcasting Corporation, which began with an attempt to find a basis for the design of earth systems. This led to general results which have been applied to the study of aerial and propagation problems by many other workers, of whom J. R. Wait is worthy of special mention. In addition to surveying this work I have included some hitherto unpublished applications.

In theoretical work the object should always be to form a physical picture, and to keep this in view as long as possible. Once this picture is lost in purely mathematical manipulations, involving quantities whose physical significance is obscure, it becomes difficult to judge the validity of approximations and to perceive the possibility of simplification. For this reason I have devoted more space to network theorems, and to their relationship to field theorems, than might otherwise appear appropriate to a monograph in this series.

I am most grateful to my wife, Ruth, for secretarial assistance. Thanks are due to the Director of Engineering of the B.B.C. for permission to publish.

Tadworth, Surrey.   G. D. MONTEATH

PRINCIPAL SYMBOLS AND CONVENTIONS

RATIONALIZED mks units are used throughout.

All field components are periodic; the time factor $\exp(j\omega t)$ is suppressed.

A prime usually indicates the value taken by a quantity following a change whose effect is being studied.

A, B	terminal pairs, or aerials connected to them. (As subscripts A and B indicate that field components result from the action of sources connected to A and B)
$\langle a, b \rangle$	"reaction" (Rumsey) between sources a and b
a	radius of the Earth (m)
$\boldsymbol{B}$	magnetic flux density (volt-seconds/m^2)
$\boldsymbol{D}$	electric displacement (coulombs/m^2)
$\mathrm{d}S$	element of area (m^2)
$\mathrm{d}s$	element of length (m)
$\mathrm{d}v$	element of volume (m^3)
$\boldsymbol{E}$	electric field (volts/m)
$\boldsymbol{e}$	electric field per unit input current (ohms/m)
Ei	exponential integral (defined by eqn. 7.16)
erfc	error function complement (defined by eqn. 4.25)
G	attenuation factor
$\boldsymbol{H}$	magnetic field (amps/m)
$\boldsymbol{h}$	magnetic field per unit input current (m^{-1})
I	current (amps)
i	current per unit input current
$\mathbf{i}, \mathbf{j}, \mathbf{k}$	unit vectors in the directions of the x, y, z axes
Im	the imaginary part of
$\boldsymbol{J}$	current density (amps/m^2)
j	$\sqrt{(-1)}$

ix

log	logarithm to base e
l	length of a Hertzian dipole or of a vertical aerial (m)
l, m, n	direction cosines relative to the x, y, z axes
M	magnetic current density (volts/m^2)
$\mathbf{n}$	unit vector normal to a surface
P	a point on a surface
P	numerical distance (defined by eqn. 8.19)
r	radius vector (m)
$\hat{r}$	unit vector in the direction of r
r_A, r_B	distance of a point from A, B (m)
R_A, R_B	special value of r_A, r_B
Re	the real part of
S, T	surfaces
t	as subscript indicates a field component tangential to a surface
V	potential difference (volts)
v	potential difference per unit input current (ohms)
v	a volume
x, y, z	Cartesian coordinates (m)
Y	admittance (siemens)
$Z = R + jX$	impedance (ohms)
$\mathscr{Z}$	line impedance (ohm . m)
z	internal impedance of a wire (ohms/m)
Z_{AB}	mutual impedance between A and B (ohms)
$j\beta$	propagation constant (m^{-1}). β may be complex.
$j\beta_0$	propagation constant of free space (m^{-1})
$\varepsilon = \varepsilon_0 \varepsilon_r$	permittivity (farads/m)
$[\varepsilon]$	permittivity tensor
ε_0	permittivity of free space (8.85×10^{-12} farads/m)
η	intrinsic impedance or surface impedance (ohms)
η_0	intrinsic impedance of free space (377 ohms)
λ	wavelength (m)
μ	permeability (henrys/m)
$[\mu]$	permeability tensor
μ_0	permeability of free space (1.26×10^{-6} henrys/m)

ϱ, ϕ	cylindrical polar coordinates
ϱ	reflection coefficient
ϱ_0	radius of an earth system (m)
σ	conductivity (siemens/m)
ω	angular frequency (radians/s)

Chapter 1

INTRODUCTION

IN a complex world any simplification is welcome, and principles of symmetry have always seemed particularly satisfying. The electromagnetic reciprocity principle forfeits some of this appeal because its application is not quite universal, and because it appeared not as a basic hypothesis but as a deduction from more fundamental principles already known, but its utility is beyond question.

The simplest statement of the principle in electrical terms was made by Lord Rayleigh (1894) as follows:

"If A and B be two electric circuits in the neighbourhood of any number of others, C, D, ..., whether closed or terminating in condensers, and a given periodic current be excited in A by the necessary electro-motive force, the induced electro-motive force in B is the same as it would be in A, if the parts of A and B were interchanged."

Rayleigh's derivation was from a theorem in which e.m.f. and current were replaced by more general quantities—for example, mechanical force and velocity—and it cannot be summarized briefly. Here we shall be concerned only with electromagnetic phenomena, and it will be found more convenient to deduce the result from an electromagnetic field theorem. This approach was first adopted by Lorentz (1895).

It frequently happens that of two reciprocal theoretical problems—for example, two problems in wave propagation that differ only in the interchange of transmitting and receiving aerials—one appears difficult while the other is easy. A simple example, attributed by Ballantine (1928) to T. L. Eckersley, is illustrated in Fig. 1.1. The problem is to determine the vertical radiation pattern of a transmitting aerial A as modified by imperfectly conducting ground below it. A direct attack entails the decomposition of the spherical waves diverging from A into an angular spectrum of plane waves, whose reflection at the ground can be evaluated in terms of the Fresnel reflection coefficient, which is applicable only to plane waves. The contributions of the reflected plane waves to the field at some distant point B may be

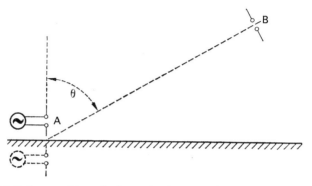

Fig. 1.1. Influence of imperfectly conducting ground on the vertical radiation pattern of an aerial.

summed in an integral. The principle of stationary phase then leads to the conclusion that the Fresnel reflection coefficient for only one of the plane waves—that indicated by geometrical optics—need have been considered. The effect of the ground proves to be represented in terms of an image carrying a current which is reduced in amplitude and modified in phase according to the Fresnel reflection coefficient appropriate to the angle of incidence θ. This last result would have been perceived at once had we considered the reciprocal problem of a receiving aerial at A and a transmitting aerial at B. Since in this case the source is distant, the waves incident on the ground may be regarded as plane, so that the Fresnel reflection coefficient can be applied immediately.

The reason for applying the term "reciprocity" or "reciprocal" to the simple theorem of Rayleigh's quoted above is clear, but the reciprocal nature of more general field theorems is less obvious. It may therefore be helpful to begin by showing (without proof) how the field theorems arise as natural extensions of the simple theorem, although to prove the results it is more convenient to proceed in the reverse direction, beginning with the field theorems.

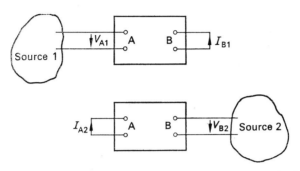

FIG. 1.2. Reciprocity of mutual admittance (eqns. (1.1) and (1.2)).

Figure 1.2 shows a two-port network having two terminal pairs A and B. Firstly some kind of source (No. 1), wholly outside the network, is connected to terminals A while terminals B are short-circuited. It is supposed that the operation of Source 1 causes a potential difference V_{A1} to exist between terminals A and a current I_{B1} to flow between terminals B. Secondly, source No. 2 is connected to terminals B, causing a potential difference V_{B2} and a current I_{A2} as shown.† Then:

$$\frac{I_{B1}}{V_{A1}} = \frac{I_{A2}}{V_{B2}} \qquad (1.1)$$

This equation states the reciprocity of mutual admittance, the expression on either side being the mutual admittance between the pairs of terminals. It may be written:

$$V_{A1}I_{A2} = V_{B2}I_{B1} \qquad (1.2)$$

† The sign convention for currents and potential differences is indicated by arrows, although we are in general concerned with alternating quantities.

This result may be generalized by no longer regarding the sources as spatially separated, and supposing each source to be connected to both terminal-pairs, though allowing only one source to operate at a time. Figure 1.3 shows the situation in which either source is connected to both terminal pairs, source No. 1 causing currents and potential differences I_{A1}, I_{B1}, V_{A1}, V_{B1} and source No. 2 causing currents and

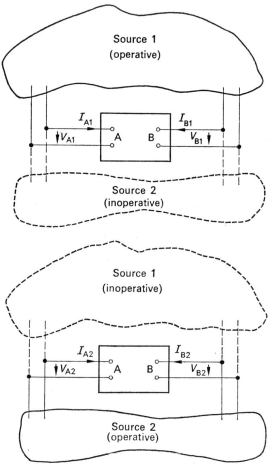

Fig. 1.3. More general two-port reciprocity theorem (eqn. (1.3)).

potential differences I_{A2}, I_{B2}, V_{A2}, V_{B2} respectively. Then eqn. (1.2) may be generalized to:

$$V_{A1}I_{A2} + V_{B1}I_{B2} = V_{B2}I_{B1} + V_{A2}I_{A1} \tag{1.3}$$

This result may be generalized further to allow the network to contain any number of terminal pairs A, B, C ..., any or all of them being connected to each source. Moreover, the network may be thought of simply as any closed surface which contains none of the sources and across which no electromagnetic influence operates, save by balanced pairs of conductors (corresponding to the terminal pairs) passing through it. If as before the currents and potential differences in conductors A, B, C ... resulting from the operation of source 1 are I_{A1} and V_{A1}, I_{B1} and V_{B1} etc., and similarly for source 2, then eqn. (1.3) may be generalized to:

$$\sum_{k=A,B...} (V_{k1}I_{k2} - V_{k2}I_{k1}) = 0 \tag{1.4}$$

Further generalization requires replacing the concepts of current and potential difference by fields. The potential difference between a pair of conductors and the current carried by them may be expressed in terms of the electric and magnetic field components tangential to any surface through which they pass. Moreover, in a transmission line carrying TEM waves the electric and magnetic fields are orthogonal. It is not therefore surprising that in eqn. (1.4) the product of a potential difference and a current may be replaced by the vector product of electric and magnetic fields, while the summation is replaced by an integral. The theorem may then be generalized as follows:

Let two systems of sources (1) and (2) operate in a linear and passive medium. Let (1) alone give rise to electric and magnetic fields E_1 and H_1, and let (2) alone give rise to electric and magnetic fields E_2 and H_2. Then if S is a closed surface containing either all or none of the sources:

$$\iint_S (E_1 \times H_2 - E_2 \times H_1) \cdot \mathbf{n} \, dS = 0 \tag{1.5}$$

where $\mathbf{n}$ is a vector in the direction of the normal to S.

This result was referred to by Ballantine (1929) as "Corollary I" to the reciprocity principle.

Up to this point the equations have not been concerned with the region in which the sources operate, but only with conditions on the surface surrounding them. An alternative approach is to express eqn. (1.4) in the form of an integral over a volume which contains all the sources. For this purpose the sources will be regarded as distributions of impressed current density, having the dimensions of current per unit area; for example one might suppose charged particles to be moved by some kind of mechanical force. Then the theorem becomes:

Let two distributions of impressed current density J_1 and J_2 operate in a linear and passive medium and let them give rise respectively to electric fields E_1 and E_2 respectively. Then:

$$\iiint (E_1 . J_2 - E_2 . J_1)\, dv = 0 \qquad (1.6)$$

where the integral is to be taken over all space in which the integrand is significant.

This result will be generalized to take account of impressed magnetic current as well as electric current.

In the following chapter the field theorems will be derived for an isotropic medium, and the network theorems will be deduced; some applications of network theorems will be discussed in Chapter 3. Chapters 4 to 9 are concerned with a formulation of Huygens' Principle and with perturbation methods, deduced from the field theorems, which are applicable to a wide range of problems.

The last chapter examines the conditions required for reciprocity, considering anisotropic and non-reciprocal media.

Chapter 2

DERIVATION

BEFORE deriving a statement of the electromagnetic reciprocity principle in terms of fields it is necessary to decide how variation of the fields with time is to be taken into account, what restrictions are to be placed upon the medium, and what kind of source is envisaged. As regards time, it will be supposed that all field components are proportional to a factor $\exp{(j\omega t)}$, since this involves no real loss of generality (any realizable time function may be synthesized as a Fourier integral), and since it facilitates generality in other respects. In particular it permits a conductivity σ to be taken into account by assigning an imaginary component $\sigma/j\omega$ to the permittivity. The medium will be regarded as described in terms of linear, scalar† and time-independent permittivity and permeability, but both these quantities will in general be complex and will vary from point to point. Thus conductors, and even linear and passive circuits containing resistors, capacitors, etc., may all be regarded as forming part of a non-uniform medium rather than as extraneous things inserted into it. For example, a transmitting aerial would not be regarded as a source, but as part of the medium, although a source would be connected to its terminals.

Alternative sources are available. Some workers have used as source a distribution of "impressed e.m.f.", but an impressed electric current seems easier to visualize, since free electric charges exist and one can imagine them to be moved mechanically. No difficulty is occasioned if a distribution of impressed "magnetic current" is also assumed, although a steady magnetic current cannot exist.

† It will be shown in Chapter 10 that the restriction to scalar permittivity and permeability may be relaxed to some extent.

7

Four of Maxwell's equations may be written as:

$$\operatorname{curl} H = j\omega D + J \tag{2.1}$$

$$\operatorname{curl} E = -j\omega B - M \tag{2.2}$$

$$B = \mu H \tag{2.3}$$

$$D = \varepsilon E \tag{2.4}$$

where E and H are electric and magnetic field strengths, D and B are electric displacement and magnetic flux density, J and M are the (vector) densities of impressed electric and magnetic current, and ε and μ are the permittivity and permeability. All these quantities may be complex.

Suppose that distributions of impressed current J_1, M_1 give rise to field components E_1, H_1, D_1, B_1 and that distributions J_2, M_2 give rise to field components E_2, H_2, D_2, B_2.

Using eqns. (2.1) and (2.2) together with the identity

$$\operatorname{div}(X \times Y) = Y \cdot \operatorname{curl} X - X \cdot \operatorname{curl} Y \tag{2.5}$$

we obtain

$$\begin{aligned}
\operatorname{div}(E_1 \times H_2 - E_2 \times H_1) = &-E_1 \cdot J_2 + E_2 \cdot J_1 + H_1 \cdot M_2 - H_2 \cdot M_1 \\
&- j\omega(E_1 \cdot D_2 - E_2 \cdot D_1) \\
&+ j\omega(H_1 \cdot B_2 - H_2 \cdot B_1)
\end{aligned} \tag{2.6}$$

Equations (2.3) and (2.4) enable the last two terms on the right-hand side to be eliminated, giving

$$\begin{aligned}
\operatorname{div}(E_1 \times H_2 - E_2 \times H_1) = &-E_1 \cdot J_2 + E_2 \cdot J_1 + H_1 \cdot M_2 \\
&- H_2 \cdot M_1
\end{aligned} \tag{2.7}$$

Both sides of this equation are then integrated over a volume v enclosed by a surface S. The divergence theorem gives:

$$\begin{aligned}
\iint_S &(E_1 \times H_2 - E_2 \times H_1) \cdot \mathbf{n} \, dS \\
&= \iiint_v (-E_1 \cdot J_2 + E_2 \cdot J_1 + H_1 \cdot M_2 - H_2 \cdot M_1) \, dv \\
&= W \quad \text{(say)}
\end{aligned} \tag{2.8}$$

where $\mathbf{n}$ is a unit vector directed along the outward normal to S.

It will now be shown that W is zero, provided that S encloses all the sources, but to do so a further assumption must be made. It will be assumed that the sources are confined within a finite volume and that the medium is uniform at sufficiently great distances from them. More precisely, we assume that it is possible to draw a sphere (say of radius a) such that all sources are inside it while the medium is uniform outside it. These assumptions do not exclude any practical situation provided that we do not wish to apply the results on a cosmological scale.

Now suppose that S is the surface of a sphere which is concentric with that enclosing the sources but whose radius R tends to infinity. The quantities $E_1 \times H_2$ and $E_2 \times H_1$ will eventually tend to zero as R^{-2} while the area of the surface S increases as R^2. It follows that the integrals

$$\iint_S (E_1 \times H_2) . \mathbf{n} \, dS \qquad \text{and} \qquad \iint_S (E_2 \times H_1) . \mathbf{n} \, dS$$

will remain bounded as the radius R tends to infinity. However, a further factor operates since as the radius increases the fields over any finite part of S must approach more and more nearly a configuration appropriate to outwardly directed plane waves. (This is known as "Sommerfeld's radiation condition".) $E_1 \times H_2$ and $E_2 \times H_1$ must therefore each tend to $\eta^{-1} (E_1 . E_2) \hat{r}$ where $\hat{r}$ is a unit vector directed radially outwards, and $\eta = \sqrt{(\mu/\varepsilon)}$ is the intrinsic impedance of the medium. The fact that both these vector products tend towards the same quantity means that their difference, the integrand on the left-hand side of eqn. (2.8), tends to zero more rapidly than R^{-2}. W must therefore tend to zero.

The foregoing argument has established that, on reasonable assumptions, the quantity W defined in eqn. (2.8) is zero provided that the surface S is a sufficiently large sphere. But the right-hand side of eqn. (2.8) must be zero for any volume containing no sources. It follows that W is zero for any surface enclosing all sources. To sum up, it has been established that

$$\iint_S (E_1 \times H_2 - E_2 \times H_1) . \mathbf{n} \, dS = 0 \qquad (1.5, 2.9)$$

and that

$$\iiint_v (E_1 . J_2 - E_2 . J_1 - H_1 . M_2 + H_2 . M_1) \, dv = 0 \quad (2.10)$$

provided that the volume v enclosed by the surface S includes either all of the sources or no part of either source. Equation (2.10) is a generalization of eqn. (1.6).

It is permissible to generalize these results by dividing v into two parts, v_1 and v_2, enclosed by closed surfaces S_1 and S_2 respectively, and using a surface integral for one and a volume integral for the other. Thus

$$\iint_{S_1} (E_1 \times H_2 - E_2 \times H_1) . \, n \, dS$$

$$- \iiint_{v_2} (E_1 . J_2 - E_2 . J_1 - H_1 . M_2 + H_2 . M_1) \, dv = 0 \quad (2.11)$$

In order to deduce circuit theorems from field theorems we must introduce the concept of a pair of terminals, which is the basis of all circuit theory. The essential condition for its validity is that if some source or load is connected to a terminal-pair, the current that flows between the terminals, and the potential difference between them, are well-defined quantities. (It is assumed that only a balanced, or push–pull, current is permitted to flow.) It is not difficult to see how this condition may be violated, for if the terminals are so large that their capacitance is significant at the highest frequency of interest the total current will depend on just where in the terminals current is supposed to be measured, since it may include all, some, or none of the current flowing in this capacitance. Moreover, if the terminals have appreciable inductance, then the potential difference between them will depend on the path along which the potential difference is supposed to be measured, since potential difference is defined as the line integral of electric field strength. It is, however, clear that if all the dimensions of the terminal-pair are progressively reduced, while keeping its form unchanged, the uncertainty in current and potential difference must become progressively smaller. It follows that, irrespective of the form of a pair of conductors, it may be regarded as a terminal-pair provided that all its dimensions are sufficiently small.† Since the current and potential difference flowing into and existing between the conductors will not then depend on their form, any convenient form may be considered.

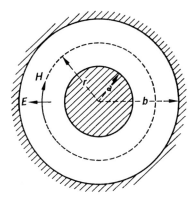

FIG. 2.1. A coaxial terminal-pair.

For example, Fig. 2.1 represents a terminal-pair formed by the conductors of a coaxial transmission line, viewed in some plane that is perpendicular to the axis and sufficiently remote, in relation to the larger diameter, from the ends of the line for the fields to correspond only to transverse electromagnetic waves. (The transverse dimensions are assumed to be small enough to exclude propagating waveguide modes.) It will be supposed that when viewing the figure we are looking towards the network of which the transmission line forms a terminal-pair. The electric and magnetic fields will then be mutually perpendicular as shown.

Suppose that the line carries a current I (flowing into the paper in the inner conductor) and that the potential difference between its conductors is V, taking the inner conductor to be positive, so that the

† It is possible to generalize the concept to include a transverse plane in any transmission line or waveguide carrying only one mode.

potential difference opposes the current when both are real and positive. Since the electric field strength E is inversely proportional to the radius and since its integral along a radius from inner to outer conductor must be equal to V, it may be shown that

$$E(r) = \frac{V}{r \log (b/a)}$$

Moreover, since the line integral of H in a path surrounding the inner conductor must equal the current flowing,

$$H = I/2\pi r$$

It follows that if S is a plane normal to the axis

$$\iint_S (E \times H) . \mathbf{n} \, dS = \iint_S EH \, dS$$

$$= \int_a^b \frac{V}{r \log (b/a)} . \frac{I}{2\pi r} . 2\pi r \, dr = VI \quad (2.12)$$

where $\mathbf{n}$ is a unit vector normal to S, i.e. parallel to the axis of the transmission line, and directed into the paper in Fig. 2.1. The sense of $\mathbf{n}$ is related to the sign conventions for V and I so that it corresponds to the direction in which power flows when V and I are real and positive. This result does not depend on the electric and magnetic fields being due to the same set of sources or even simultaneous.

Equation (2.12) enables the surface integral in eqns. (2.9) and (2.11) to be simplified by taking advantage of any concentration of field associated with balanced pairs of conductors passing through the surface of integration. If the only field components contributing significantly to the surface integral are those associated with the conductor pairs (these being small enough in their transverse dimensions to be regarded as terminal-pairs) then the situation may be treated as a network problem.

Figure 2.2 shows a network having a number of terminal-pairs A, B ... N, which is surrounded by a closed surface S intersecting the conductors connecting the terminals. (More precisely we may think of the terminals as formed by the intersection of S with the conductors.) Suppose now that a system of sources (1) wholly outside S causes electric and magnetic field components E_1, H_1 and similarly for a second system of sources (2).

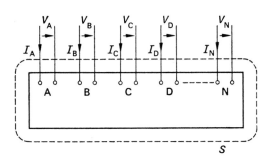

FIG. 2.2. Reciprocity for a multiport network.

Since S excludes all the sources eqn. (2.9) is satisfied. It will now be assumed that significant contributions to the integral are made only by the fields in the immediate vicinity of the terminal pairs. This condition would be satisfied if the fields elsewhere on S were negligible, or if either the electric or the magnetic fields were everywhere normal to S. The former condition would hold if S were the surface of a metal box enclosing the network, apart from small holes for the terminals. The network theorem stated as eqn. (1.4) follows from eqns. (2.9) and (2.12).

If the network has only two terminal-pairs A and B eqn. (1.4) simplifies to

$$V_{A1}I_{A2} + V_{B1}I_{B2} = V_{A2}I_{A1} + V_{B2}I_{B1} \qquad (1.3, 2.13)$$

Three useful reciprocity theorems illustrated in Fig. 2.3 may be derived from this equation by putting

$$V_{A2} = V_{B1} = 0$$

to obtain

$$I_{B1}/V_{A1} = I_{A2}/V_{B2} \qquad (2.14)$$

(reciprocity of mutual admittance) or by putting

$$I_{A2} = I_{B1} = 0$$

to obtain

$$V_{B1}/I_{A1} = V_{A2}/I_{B2} \qquad (2.15)$$

(reciprocity of mutual impedance) or finally by putting

$$I_{A1} = 0 \qquad \text{and} \qquad V_{B2} = 0$$

to obtain

$$V_{A1}/V_{B1} = -I_{B2}/I_{A2} \qquad (2.16)$$

(reciprocity of transfer constants).

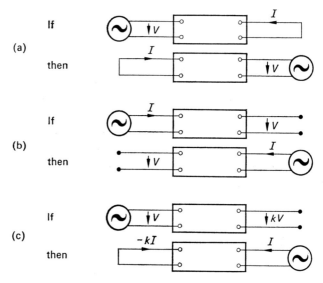

FIG. 2.3. Reciprocity theorems for two-port networks. (a) Reciprocity of mutual admittance (eqn. (2.14)). (b) Reciprocity of mutual impedance (eqn. (2.15)). (c) Reciprocity of transfer constants (eqn. (2.16)). (The converse is also true.)

Chapter 3

SOME APPLICATIONS
OF THE NETWORK THEOREMS

IT should be emphasized that the network theorems have been so called only because they express reciprocity between terminal pairs. Since they have been derived from a field theorem their application is not confined to networks made up of lumped components, and they may, for example, be applied to aerials coupled together by radiation. The Introduction mentioned the problem of a dipole above imperfectly conducting ground, in which calculation of the vertical radiation pattern is simplified by supposing that the dipole is used for reception rather than transmission. This is an example of the equality of the radiation patterns of an aerial when used for transmission and reception (Brown, J., 1958), a most useful principle but one which is sometimes misapplied. The mistake commonly made is to suppose that reciprocity permits the interchange of transmitting and receiving *aerials*, even when these are different, whereas it is only a source and a detector connected to the aerials that may be interchanged. There are, of course, many cases in which the distinction is not important.

Figure 3.1 shows an insulated loop aerial A on a submerged submarine. It will be supposed that it is to be used for transmission at a suitably low frequency—e.g. 20 kHz, and that we require to determine the field strength above the sea (for a given current flowing in the loop) at some point B a few miles distant. For simplicity we may suppose that the result is known for the case when the loop is just above the surface and that we wish to find the ratio in which the field is diminished by submerging the loop.

As in the problem mentioned in the Introduction, a direct attack involves the arrival of spherical waves at a plane interface, but in this case further complication results from the fact that these waves are propagated in a conducting medium having a complex propagation constant. This difficulty is avoided by supposing A to be used for the reception of signals radiated from B. Using the reciprocity of mutual impedance we consider the open-circuit potential difference between the terminals of A (which is proportional to the magnetic field strength) due to unit current flowing into the terminals of B.

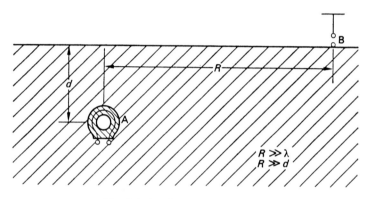

FIG. 3.1. A submerged loop aerial.

Just above the surface the fields will be substantially the same as if the sea were a perfect conductor and will correspond to vertically polarized† waves proceeding outwards from B. The magnetic vector will be tangential to the surface and continuous across it. To derive the fields below the surface we may regard the distribution of horizontal magnetic field over the surface as a source of waves propagated downwards.

The intrinsic propagation constant $j\beta_s$ of sea water at low frequencies is given by

$$j\beta_s \simeq (j\omega\mu_0\sigma_s)^{1/2} \tag{3.1}$$

† The polarization refers to the electric vector.

where μ_0 is the permeability of free space and σ_s the conductivity of sea water. β_s is enormously greater in magnitude than the propagation constant of free space.

Now $|\beta_s|^{-1}$, which is small, provides a standard of length for phenomena in the sea. It follows that, from the standpoint of the sea, the tangential magnetic field associated with waves propagated in the air varies very slowly from point to point of the surface, and may be regarded as uniform. The fields in the sea may therefore be regarded as associated with uniform plane waves propagated vertically downwards, so that all field components will vary with the depth z in proportion to $\exp(-j\beta_s z)$. Applying reciprocity, it follows that submergence of a loop transmitting aerial to a depth d will reduce the field (for a given input current) propagated to some distant point above the surface in proportion to a complex factor $\exp(-j\beta_s d)$.

In both examples the problem was simplified by choosing whichever one of two reciprocal arrangements involved plane waves rather than spherical waves incident upon a plane surface. The reverse is true of the problem of a small dipole embedded at the centre of a dielectric sphere. In this case it would be easier to regard the dipole as a transmitting aerial and consider spherical waves incident on the spherical boundary surface.

Another problem involving a curved boundary surface is the calculation of the radiation pattern of an aerial near to a conducting cylinder—for example a cylindrical mast supporting the aerial.† In this case it is easier to suppose the aerial to be used for reception, even though this entails supposing plane waves from a distant source to be incident upon the cylindrical surface. Expansion of plane waves in terms of an infinite series of cylindrical waves (coaxial with the conducting cylinder) presents little difficulty.

In the examples already considered the emphasis was placed not on the aerial element—for example a dipole or loop—but upon its environment. The reciprocity principle can also effect a useful simplification when considering the element itself. Figure 3.2 illustrates

---

† See, for example, Jordan and Balmain (1968), p. 530.

the "induced-e.m.f. method" (Pistolkors, 1929) of determining the open-circuit potential difference at the terminals of a thin-wire receiving aerial.

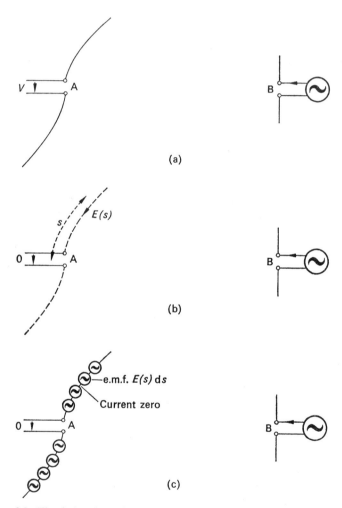

(a)

(b)

(c)

FIG. 3.2. The induced-e.m.f. method. (a) The situation to be considered. (b) The aerial becomes non-conducting. (c) The aerial again conducts, but current is inhibited by impressed e.m.f.s.

Referring to Fig. 3.2 (a) it will be supposed that fields are set up by another aerial with terminals B, and that we require to determine the open-circuit potential difference V between terminals A. Three conditions are shown:

In Fig. 3.2 (a) the receiving aerial is present and, as a result of radiation from the aerial connected to B there is a potential difference V between terminals A. In Fig. 3.2 (b) the wire of which the receiving aerial is made is supposed to have become non-conducting, and there now exists a component $E(s)$ of electric field strength tangential to it where s is distance measured along the wire from some convenient origin. Under this condition the potential difference between terminals A is negligible, since these terminals are not connected to anything. In Fig. 3.2 (c) the wire is again supposed to be a conductor, but now any current is supposed to be inhibited by inserting in each elementary length ds of the wire a generator of e.m.f. equal to $E(s) ds$. Since the wire carries no current the potential difference between terminals A will again be negligible.

It is clear that the effect of the elementary generators $E(s) ds$ is to cancel the effect of the incident fields. V is therefore the potential difference that would be produced by a set of elementary generators $-E(s) ds$ operating in series with the wire. It is at this point that the reciprocity principle is invoked in order to determine the potential difference dV at the open-circuit terminals due to a single elementary generator of e.m.f. $-E(s) ds$ operating in series with the aerial. For this purpose we use the reciprocity of transfer constant (see eqn. (2.16) and Fig. 2.3 (c)) obtaining the result

$$dV = i_T(s)\, E(s)\, ds \qquad (3.2)$$

where $i_T(s)$ is the current that would flow in the aerial at s if it were treated as a transmitting aerial and energized by injecting unit current between its terminals.

It follows that

$$V = -\int E(s)\, i_T(s)\, ds \qquad (3.3)$$

when the integral is taken over the length of the aerial. It sometimes seems paradoxical that it would be the current distribution on a *transmitting* aerial that is required to determine the behaviour of a *receiving* aerial. It must however be remembered that the current distribution on a transmitting aerial is a property of the aerial itself, whereas that on a receiving aerial depends on the configuration of the incident field—for example, it will generally depend on the orientation of the aerial relative to the field—and on the impedance connected to the terminals.

The induced-e.m.f. method has been used by Carter (1932) to determine the mutual impedance between thin-wire dipoles. The first dipole

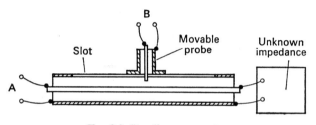

FIG. 3.3. Standing-wave meter.

is supposed to be energized by injecting unit current into its terminals, and from a knowledge of the current distribution the electric field strength along the second dipole (in that dipole's absence) is calculated. The open-circuit potential difference between the terminals of the second dipole is then obtained from eqn. (3.3), using a knowledge of the current distribution along the second dipole. Carter also derived the self-impedance of a thin-wire dipole, taking this to be a special case of mutual impedance.

A further class of applications of the network relations is to a measuring instrument such as a bridge having two terminal pairs to which are connected a source and a detector (Monteath, 1959). It can usually be shown that either of the two reciprocal configurations will, in principle at least, give the same result, although one configuration may have practical advantages whereas the other is more easily understood. An excellent example is a standing-wave meter used for impedance measurement, which is illustrated in Fig. 3.3.

The unknown is connected to one end of a uniform transmission line to the inner conductor of which a movable probe is coupled by a very small capacity. The behaviour of this device is not difficult to understand in either of the two reciprocal configurations, but its operation is visualized with particular ease if terminals A are supposed to be connected to the source while terminals B are connected to the detector, and this is the configuration usually employed. Often the detector is a crystal detector or meter mounted on the moving carriage bearing the probe, but a convenient alternative is to use a flexible coaxial cable to connect the probe to a receiver. When this arrangement is used it is easy to interchange the source and detector.

When the source is connected to terminals A one can visualize the way in which reflection at the unknown impedance causes standing waves of potential difference, and can regard the probe as a means of measuring this potential difference. (The impedance is determined from the maximum and minimum values, and the position of the minimum.) The reciprocal configuration in which the source is connected to the probe is less easily understood, and is therefore rarely used, although it sometimes has practical advantages. For example, if the unknown impedance is non-linear, like a crystal mixer, and if its impedance is to be determined for small signals, the source is best connected to B, where it is coupled less strongly to the unknown. Another situation in which the unconventional configuration is better is when the unknown is an aerial and the detector—for example a receiver—is badly screened. Again it is desirable to connect the source to the terminals less strongly coupled to the unknown. The conventional configuration is of course better when it is the source that is badly screened.

There are many devices for impedance measurement at high frequencies, and most of them have a "source" label fitted to the terminals most strongly coupled to the unknown. It is intriguing to note that when one configuration is better it is not usually that indicated by the labels. Further consideration of this point, in relation to the standing-wave meter, sheds some light on the paradox of why one reciprocal configuration is often more easily understood than the other.

If it is supposed that the source is connected to A, and if the capacitance between the probe and the inner conductor of the transmission line is small, it is easy to visualize the standing-wave pattern because the small probe capacitance does not disturb it. On the other hand if the source is connected to B it is impossible to neglect the influence of the probe on the field distribution, for the fields are excited by the probe. In fact it is usually true that a device incorporating a source and detector is most easily understood when the detector is weakly coupled, so that this coupling causes little disturbance. Textbooks naturally describe the configuration most easily understood, and manufacturers fix SOURCE and DETECTOR labels in accordance with the textbooks.

Chapter 4

HUYGENS' PRINCIPLE

4.1 *Introductory*

Huygens' Principle states that the position of a wavefront, and the magnitude of the "disturbance" at each point of it, may be determined from the wavefront at any earlier time. Each element of the earlier wavefront is regarded as a source, and the contributions of all these sources, when summed with due regard to phase, gives the disturbance at any point in the later wavefront. Huygens was not able to formulate his principle precisely, and at the time it was not possible to overcome certain difficulties—in particular the fact that the wavefront always continues to advance instead of propagating in both directions from any intermediate position—save by rather arbitrary assumptions. Much later workers have placed the principle on a rigorous theoretical basis, both for scalar wave motion and for electromagnetic waves. In the latter case Kottler's formulae† provide the best-known representation. The result is to express the field at some point P (Fig. 4.1) in terms of a surface integral over a closed surface S separating P from the source; the integral contains the fields on this surface and their spatial derivatives. When Huygens' Principle has been expressed exactly in this way it is found to have lost much of its original simplicity and it no longer seems to offer the same insight into the way in which waves are propagated. Since Maxwell's equations are required to produce an exact expression of Huygens' Principle, one might as well deduce the phenomena of wave propagation from these equations directly.

† Baker and Copson (1953), p. 117.

In fact the use of Huygens' Principle in modern times is not so much to aid the understanding of wave propagation as to obtain approximate solutions of diffraction problems. For example, if part of the surface S is blocked out by some kind of opaque screen S_1, as

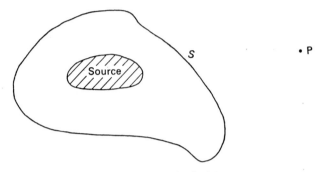

FIG. 4.1. Huygens' Principle.

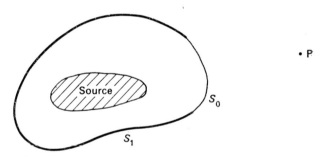

FIG. 4.2. Application of Huygens' Principle to a diffraction problem.

shown in Fig. 4.2, leaving an aperture S_0, the integral referred to above is taken only over the aperture S_0. Unfortunately the fields over S_0 will have been influenced by the presence of the screen, and it is no less difficult to calculate them on S_0 than at P or elsewhere. It is, however, often possible to obtain a solution of sufficient accuracy by assuming that the fields are zero on the outer surface of S_1 and that their values on S_0 are unaffected by the screen; this procedure is referred to as "classical" diffraction theory.

A useful simplification may be effected by applying the reciprocity principle to propagation between the surface S_0 and the point P. Thus instead of regarding each element of S_0 as a source and computing the fields due to it at P, we regard P—which may be thought of as some kind of aerial—as a source and compute its fields at every point of S_0. Once this procedure is adopted the distinction between source and receiving point is removed; what is done is to determine the coupling between two aerials in terms of an integral over a surface separating them. In furtherance of this approach there will be derived an expression for the mutual impedance between two pairs of terminals, which may be the terminals of two aerials, in terms of an integral over a surface separating them. In spite of its simplicity this way of expressing Huygens' Principle, unlike Kottler's formulae, is applicable to inhomogeneous media.

4.2 A Mutual-impedance Formula

Figure 4.3 shows the two terminal-pairs, A and B, which are separated by a closed surface S. A and B may be coupled together, for example, by conductors or an electrical network passing through S, or by radiation between aerials connected to them. Also shown are two generators of infinite internal impedance, which are connected to A

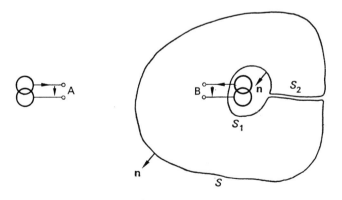

FIG. 4.3

and B and may be operated independently. In order to form a closed surface which excludes all sources a small closed surface S_1 will be supposed to surround the generator connected to B. S and S_1 may be treated as a single closed surface: this procedure is justified by supposing a third surface S_2 in the form of a thin tube to join S and S_1 together. If the tube is thin enough its contribution to surface integrals may be neglected.

Sign conventions for currents and potential differences are indicated by arrows in Fig. 4.3. Suppose that the impressment of unit current between terminals A with terminals B open-circuit results in electric and magnetic fields e_A, h_A, and that the impressment of unit current between terminals B, with terminals A open-circuit, results in electric and magnetic fields e_B, h_B. Taking these two cases as the operation of sources 1 and 2 respectively in eqn. (2.9), this equation becomes

$$\iint_{S+S_1} (e_A \times h_B - e_B \times h_A) \cdot \mathbf{n}\, dS = 0 \qquad (4.1)$$

in which $\mathbf{n}$ is regarded as directed along the outward normal to S and the inward normal to S_1. This difference of sense arises because the tubular surface S_2 joins the outside of S to the inside of S_1 and vice-versa.

If now the generator connected to terminals B, and the cross-section of the connecting conductors, are supposed to be very small, the surface S_1 may also be made very small. In the limit the only significant contribution of the integral over it will be due to the fields associated with the current in the conductors and the potential difference between them. Now on S_1, e_A is associated with the open-circuit potential difference between terminals B due to unit current impressed between terminals A; this is equal to the mutual impedance Z_{AB}. h_B is associated with unit current impressed between terminals B, but h_A may be neglected because e_A and h_A are applicable only when terminals B are open-circuit. It therefore follows from eqn. (2.12) that

$$\iint_{S_1} (e_A \times h_B - e_B \times h_A) \cdot \mathbf{n}\, dS = -Z_{AB} \qquad (4.2)$$

Equation (4.1) therefore becomes

$$Z_{AB} = \iint_S (e_A \times h_B - e_B \times h_A) . \mathbf{n} \, dS \qquad (4.3)$$

where S is any closed surface completely separating A from B, the sense of $\mathbf{n}$ being from B towards A (Monteath, 1951). For all practical purposes eqn. (4.3) may be regarded as an exact expression of Huygens' Principle, and in spite of its simplicity it is remarkably general, for the medium need not be homogeneous, and may even contain conductors, resistors, etc., through which S may pass. In order to apply the equation to a diffraction problem it is necessary to imagine that the source is an aerial (with terminals A) and to suppose a second aerial (with terminals B) to be placed as a field-measuring device at the point where the diffracted field is to be determined. This second aerial could be a small dipole for determining the electric field or a small loop for determining magnetic field. The field component under consideration is then proportional to the mutual impedance.

At this point it is instructive to compare eqn. (4.3) with the well-known Fresnel–Kirchoff formula of the classical diffraction theory[†] which may be used to compute the "disturbance" F_{AB} at B due to a source at A in terms of an integral over a closed surface S surrounding A on the following assumptions:

(i) The wave motion is scalar and the source at A is isotropic.

(ii) The medium is uniform.

(iii) All points of S are many wavelengths distant from A and B.)

The Fresnel–Kirchoff formula is:

$$F_{AB} = \frac{j\beta}{4\pi} \iint_S (\cos \alpha_A - \cos \alpha_B) \exp \{-j\beta (r_A + r_B)\} \frac{dS}{r_A r_B}$$

$$(4.4)$$

where α_A, α_B, r_A and r_B are defined as in Fig. 4.4. Note that α_A and α_B

[†] Baker and Copson (1953), p. 72.

are the angles made by PA and PB with **n**, even when AP, BP, and **n** are not coplanar. The constant $j\beta/4\pi$ has been so chosen that when the integral is evaluated the result is

$$F_{AB} = \frac{1}{r_{AB}} \exp\left(-j\beta r_{AB}\right) \tag{4.5}$$

where r_{AB} is the distance AB. We may regard a source A satisfying this condition as a "unit source".

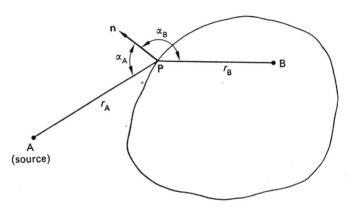

FIG. 4.4. The Fresnel–Kirchoff formula.

In order to justify the use of eqn. (4.4) for investigating diffraction through an aperture in a screen it is necessary to make a fourth assumption:

(iv) On S the disturbance F and its gradient normal to S are zero except in the aperture, where they are unaffected by the presence of the screen.

It must be emphasized that assumption (iv), which is basic to the classical approach, and which is very useful in practice, is fundamentally false for any kind of wave motion, and can never be more than an approximation. No screen can satisfy this condition exactly because the diffracted field calculated on this basis does not satisfy the wave equation.

The integrand in eqn. (4.4) contains factors $r_A^{-1} \exp(-j\beta r_A)$ and $r_B^{-1} \exp(-j\beta r_B)$ which may be regarded as the "disturbances" that would be produced at P by unit sources at A and B respectively. The angles α_A and α_B are respectively equal to the inclinations to $-\mathbf{n}$ of the directions of waves proceeding from A and B towards P. Equation (4.4) may therefore be replaced by the following statement:

Let the disturbances at P due to unit sources at A and B be F_{AP} and F_{BP} respectively, and let the directions of waves at P due to radiation from sources at A and B be respectively characterized by unit vectors $\hat{r}_A$ and $\hat{r}_B$ respectively. Then the disturbance F_{AB} at B due to a unit source at A is given by

$$F_{AB} = \frac{j\beta}{4\pi} \iint_S F_{AP}F_{BP} (\hat{r}_B - \hat{r}_A) \cdot \mathbf{n} \, dS \qquad (4.6)$$

where S is a closed surface separating A from B and $\mathbf{n}$ is the normal at P directed from B towards A.

In order to compare eqn. (4.3) with this statement we define unit vectors $\mathbf{a}$, $\mathbf{b}$ and $\mathbf{c}$ as shown in Fig. 4.5. $\mathbf{a}$ and $\mathbf{b}$ are perpendicular to

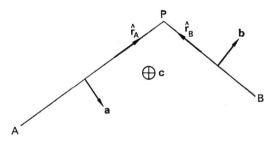

FIG. 4.5.

AP and BP respectively, lying in the plane APB. $\mathbf{c}$ is normal to that plane. It will be supposed that aerials are connected to terminals A and B and that AP and BP are both large in comparison with the wavelength and with the dimensions of the aerials. Then e_A and h_A at P will be perpendicular to each other and to r_A, and will be in the ratio η, the intrinsic impedance of the medium. We may therefore put

$$h_A = h_{Aa}a + h_{Ac}c \tag{4.7}$$

$$e_A = \eta\,(h_{Ac}a - h_{Aa}c) \tag{4.8}$$

and similarly for h_B and e_B. Substitution in eqn. (4.3) is found to give

$$Z_{AB} = \iint_S \eta\,\{(h_{Aa}h_{Bb} - h_{Ac}h_{Bc})\,(\hat{r}_B - \hat{r}_A)$$

$$+ (h_{Ac}h_{Bb} + h_{Aa}h_{Bc})\,\hat{r}_A \times \hat{r}_B\}\,.\,\mathbf{n}\,dS \tag{4.9}$$

The principal difference between eqns. (4.9) and (4.6) is due to polarization, which plays no part in the Fresnel–Kirchoff theory. If $h_{Aa}/h_{Ac} = -h_{Bb}/h_{Bc}$ we may regard the polarizations of the two aerials, *as viewed from P*, as "corresponding". There is then agreement between eqns. (4.9) and (4.6), apart from a constant factor depending on the aerial characteristics. In the special case of linear polarization F_{AP} and F_{BP} are equivalent to $\eta^{1/2}h_A$ and $\eta^{1/2}h_B$, where η may be a function of position.

The second term of the integrand in eqn. (4.9) exists only where the polarizations do not correspond, and then only when APB is not a straight line. This term is a vector directed normally to the APB plane, and its component in the $\mathbf{n}$-direction will therefore be small in any region of S over which the phase of the integrand varies slowly. For this reason it will not usually make a significant contribution to the integral.

In cases where an electromagnetic treatment is not necessary the foregoing argument justifies some generalization of the Fresnel–Kirchoff formula to inhomogeneous media. It is necessary to redefine $\hat{r}_A$ and $\hat{r}_B$ as directions of wave propagation; this implies that reflection and scattering by discontinuities are neglected. It is also necessary to neglect cross-polarization. This approach may have applications to optical systems, particularly when both diffraction and aberrations have to be taken into account. It might, for example, be advantageous to integrate over an aperture within a system of lenses. In many cases it would be permissible to compute F_{AP} and F_{BP} within the aperture by geometrical optics.

At this point it might well appear that eqn. (4.3) offers no advantage for the solution of a simple diffraction problem to which the classical theory might have been applied, since both approaches lead to the same result and involve essentially the same mathematical problems. The merit of the mutual-impedance approach based on reciprocity lies in the fact that the quantities involved in the formula have a simple physical significance, so that when approximations have to be made the validity of these can be assessed on the basis of physical experience and judgement. A convenient example is provided by the simple problem of diffraction by a plane conducting sheet with a straight edge, which will be considered in the next section.

Under certain conditions a formula similar to eqn. (4.3) may be used to determine the proportion of the power radiated by one aerial which is absorbed by a load connected to another (Robieux, 1957, 1959). This result is expressed in terms of the field components resulting from the radiation of unit power from each aerial, rather than from unit current injected between the terminals.

It will be assumed that the two aerials are only weakly coupled, so that the matching of one is unaffected by that of the other. Suppose that unit power radiated from aerial A(B), when aerial B(A) is terminated in a matched load, results in fields $E_A(E_B)$ and $H_A(H_B)$. Let the input impedances be $Z_A = R_A + jX_A$ and Z_B. Now if unit current is injected between the terminals of A, the power radiated will be equal to R_A, and the power delivered to the load of B will be $|Z_{AB}|^2/4R_B$. Bearing in mind that $E_A = e_A/\sqrt{R_A}$ and that $H_A = h_A/\sqrt{R_A}$ apart from an arbitrary phase factor, it is easily seen that the proportion k_{AB} of the power radiated by A which is absorbed by the load of B is given by

$$k_{AB} = \frac{1}{2} \left| \iint_S (E_A \times H_B - E_B \times H_A) \cdot \mathbf{n} \, dS \right|^2 \qquad (4.10)$$

4.3 *Diffraction by a Metal Sheet*

The classical diffraction theory, for example in the form of the Fresnel–Kirchoff formula (eqn. (4.4)), gives a simple approximate solution to the problem of diffraction by the straight edge of an opaque screen. In many cases this provides an adequate approximation

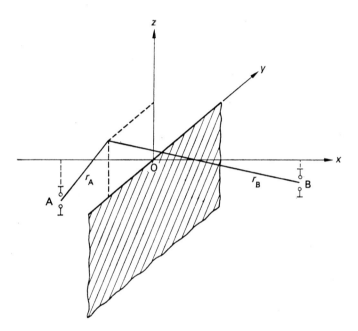

Fig. 4.6. Diffraction by a conducting half-plane.

to the diffraction of electromagnetic waves by a metal sheet, but this is not always true. Equation (4.3) may be used to provide a physical explanation for the resulting error, and for its dependence on polarization.

Figure 4.6 illustrates the problem, which has been simplified more than is strictly necessary in order to emphasize its essential features. Taking Cartesian coordinates the screen is defined by $x = 0$; $z < 0$.

Two Hertzian dipoles† A and B, polarized in the z-direction, are situated in the xz-plane, at least several wavelengths from the plane of the screen. It will be supposed that eqn. (4.3) is used to determine the mutual impedance between the dipoles, taking the surface S to be the yz plane and assuming in the first instance that the fields on this surface for $z > 0$ are unaffected by the presence of the metal sheet.

Since the dipoles are not too close to S the phase variation due to the variation of r_A and r_B dominates the integral and it is permissible to replace all factors other than the phase factor $\exp \{ -j\beta (r_A + r_B) \}$ by their values at 0, which has been chosen to be the point of slowest phase variation.

Suppose that integration is first carried out with respect to y, and that the final step is to integrate with respect to z from zero to z_1. Figure 4.7 illustrates on the Argand diagram the way in which the integral varies as z_1 tends to infinity. The point P, where OP represents the integral, moves along the curve (essentially the same as Cornu's spiral) towards the asymptotic point Q. Each element of the spiral represents the contribution to the integral of an elementary strip of the yz plane parallel to the y axis.

Now the conducting sheet can influence the fields only by reason of the current that it carries, and since the sheet is assumed to be thin this current cannot result in a magnetic field tangential to the surface of integration. It is, however, easy to see—and indeed well known from general experience—that there must be a concentration of electric field at the sharp edge of the sheet. Moreover, by analogy with a capacitive diaphragm in a waveguide one would expect the additional components of e_A and e_B near to the edge to be retarded in phase relative to the incident fields. The effect of these additional components on the integral takes the form indicated by the broken-line curve in Fig. 4.7. Z_{AB}, as represented by the vector OQ, is augmented by the vector O'O.

---

† A *Hertzian dipole* is a useful theoretical concept. It may be regarded as a thin wire, which is short compared with the wavelength, and which is loaded at the tips with spheres or discs so that the current distribution is uniform. See, for example, Jordan and Balmain (1968), p. 321.

In order to estimate the order of magnitude of OO′ we note that the disturbance of the electric field by the metal sheet will be important only within about a wavelength of the edge. Moreover, from electro-static considerations the field very near the edge must vary inversely as the square root of the distance. These considerations lead to the conclusion that OO′ must be of the same order of magnitude as a

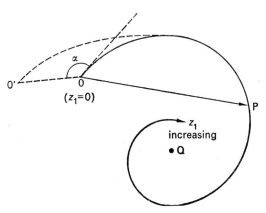

FIG. 4.7. Diffraction by a conducting half-plane. Plot of

$$\int_0^{z_1} \mathrm{d}z \int_{-\infty}^{\infty} (e_A \times h_B - e_B \times h_A) \cdot \mathbf{n}\, \mathrm{d}y$$

as a function of z_1. ——— Assuming fields undistorted by the half-plane for $z > 0$. ----- Effect of the half-plane (magnetic field parallel to the edge.)

length of a chord of the spiral corresponding to an increase of $1/\beta$ $(= \lambda/2\pi)$ in z_1. In other words the error in the classical theory is of the same order of magnitude, but not the same phase, as the effect of removing a strip of width $1/\beta$ from the edge of the sheet.

The phase of the error must be approximately as shown $(\pi/2 < \alpha < \pi)$ since the additional electric field is retarded relative to the incident field. As a result the concentration of electric field near to the edge must tend to increase the magnitude of the mutual impedance, since O′Q > OQ.

For a small angle of diffraction z_1 can change by many wavelengths to complete the first half-turn of the spiral; the effect of OO', i.e. the error in the classical theory, is then unimportant. The error becomes more pronounced as the angle of diffraction becomes greater.

A similar approach can be made when it is the electric vector that is parallel to the diffracting edge, but here the effect of currents in the sheet is to advance the phase and reduce the magnitude of the integrand for points near to the edge ($3\pi/2 < \alpha < 2\pi$), and the result is to reduce the magnitude of the mutual impedance at large angles of diffraction.

It must be emphasized that there would be little point in attempting to use the procedure outlined above to estimate the field due to diffraction by a conducting half-plane with a straight edge because exact and reasonably simple solutions are available (e.g. Clemmow, 1966). This procedure does, however, provide a useful insight into less simple configurations—for example, sheets with curved edges—for which no exact solutions exist.

4.4 Groundwave Propagation

Figure 4.8 illustrates the problem of the propagation of vertically polarized groundwaves over a plane imperfectly conducting earth. For simplicity each of the two aerials, A and B, may be regarded as the grounded equivalent of a Hertzian dipole, one terminal being connected to some kind of buried earth system while the other is connected to a short vertical wire terminated in a capacitive top, which is large enough to enable the current distribution in the vertical wire to be regarded as uniform. This problem was first solved by Sommerfeld, whose solution was equivalent to the expansion of the system of spherical waves radiated from one aerial in terms of an angular spectrum of plane waves. The effect of reflection of each plane-wave component at the ground could then be obtained in terms of the Fresnel reflection coefficient, leading to a result expressed in terms of Fresnel integrals or error functions of a complex variable. An alternative solution, permitting considerable generalization, will be discussed in Chapter 8.

Although Huygens' Principle cannot provide a substitute for the solution referred to above it is instructive to use it to obtain an approximate result which is valid in the limit when the distance between the transmitting and receiving aerials is sufficiently large to justify certain simplifying assumptions. This approach offers a useful

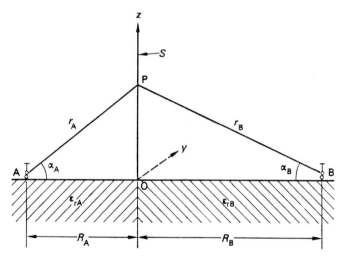

FIG. 4.8. Huygens' Principle applied to groundwave propagation over a plane earth. (The y-axis is into the paper.)

physical insight into the problem; moreover, it can be used to study certain variants which could not be tackled directly by Sommerfeld's method.

Referring to Fig. 4.8, it will be supposed that the ground is characterized by a complex permittivity ε, whose imaginary part is associated with conduction. It is convenient to write

$$\varepsilon = \varepsilon_0 \varepsilon_r$$

where ε_0 is the permittivity of free space. It will be supposed that ε_r takes values, ε_{rA} and ε_{rB} respectively, in two regions separated by a straight boundary perpendicular to AB.

Equation (4.3) will be used to express the mutual impedance

between A and B in terms of a surface integral over the vertical plane
S passing through the boundary. The simplifying assumption is that
the fields on S, due to radiation from A or B, may be computed by
ray theory. For example, the electric or magnetic field at P due to
current in A will be taken as that due to free-space radiation multiplied
by the factor $(1 + \varrho_A)$ where ϱ_A is the Fresnel reflection coefficient
appropriate to the angle of elevation. This assumption is of course
not justified for values of z that are too small, but it is known to be
true for sufficiently large values of z. It is assumed that R_A and R_B
are so large that the region of S for which z is small does not make
an important contribution to the integral. Although this procedure
has not been justified rigorously, it is nevertheless instructive to follow
it through.

In applying eqn. (4.3) the usual stationary-phase approximation
may be justified on the basis that r_A and r_B are each equal to many
wavelengths. The integral is then determined by the behaviour of the
integrand in that region of S for which α_A and α_B are small, and for
which AP and BP are nearly normal to S. On this assumption
eqn. (4.3) gives:

$$Z_{AB} \simeq K_1 \int_0^\infty dz \int_{-\infty}^\infty \frac{(1 + \varrho_A)\exp(-j\beta_0 r_A)}{r_A} \cdot \frac{(1 + \varrho_B)\exp(-j\beta_0 r_B)}{r_B} dy$$

(4.11)

where K_1 is a constant. Further approximations based on the stationary-
phase principle allow r_A and r_B in the denominator to be replaced by
R_A and R_B and to be taken outside the integrals. Moreover, in the
exponent we may write

$$r_A = (R_A^2 + y^2 + z^2)^{1/2} \simeq R_A + \frac{y^2 + z^2}{2R_A}$$

(4.12)

Equation (4.11) becomes:

$$Z_{AB} \simeq \frac{K_1}{R_A R_B} \int_0^\infty dz \int_{-\infty}^\infty (1 + \varrho_A)(1 + \varrho_B) \times$$

$$\times \exp\left\{-\frac{1}{2}j\beta_0 \left(\frac{1}{R_A} + \frac{1}{R_B}\right)(y^2 + z^2)\right\} dy \quad (4.13)$$

Integration is performed firstly with respect to y (the stationary-phase principle permitting the first two factors to be taken outside this integral) giving

$$Z_{AB} \simeq \frac{K_2}{\sqrt{R_A R_B (R_A + R_B)}} \int_0^\infty (1 + \varrho_A)(1 + \varrho_B) \times$$

$$\times \exp\left\{ -\frac{1}{2} j\beta_0 \left(\frac{1}{R_A} + \frac{1}{R_B} \right) z^2 \right\} dz \qquad (4.14)$$

where K_2 is constant.

Assuming that α_A is small and that the complex relative permittivity ε_{rA} is greater than 10 in magnitude, the reflection coefficient ϱ_A may be expressed approximately as

$$\varrho_A \simeq \frac{\sqrt{(\varepsilon_{rA} + 1)} \sin \alpha_A - 1}{\sqrt{(\varepsilon_{rA} + 1)} \sin \alpha_A + 1} \qquad (4.15)$$

and similarly for ϱ_B. (This is the approximation usual in propagation work: the field impedance normal to the ground is assumed to be the same as that appropriate to plane waves at grazing incidence.) Putting

$$\sin \alpha_A \simeq \tan \alpha_A \simeq z/R_A$$

we obtain

$$(1 + \varrho_A) \simeq \frac{2\sqrt{(\varepsilon_{rA} + 1)} z}{\sqrt{(\varepsilon_{rA} + 1)} z + R_A} \simeq 2\sqrt{(\varepsilon_{rA} + 1)} z/R_A \qquad (4.16)$$

Hence

$$Z_{AB} \simeq \frac{4K_2 \sqrt{(\varepsilon_{rA} + 1)(\varepsilon_{rB} + 1)}}{R_A R_B \sqrt{R_A R_B (R_A + R_B)}} \times$$

$$\times \int_0^\infty z^2 \exp\left\{ -\frac{1}{2} j\beta_0 \left(\frac{1}{R_A} + \frac{1}{R_B} \right) z^2 \right\} dz \qquad (4.17)$$

$$= -j^{1/2} \cdot 2\sqrt{(2\pi)} K_2 \beta_0^{-3/2} \frac{\sqrt{(\varepsilon_{rA} + 1)(\varepsilon_{rB} + 1)}}{(R_A + R_B)^2} \qquad (4.18)$$

It is convenient to express the result in terms of a groundwave attenuation factor $G = Z_{AB}/Z_{AB0}$, where Z_{AB0} is the value which Z_{AB}

THE
UNIVERSITY OF WINNIPEG
PORTAGE & BALMORAL
WINNIPEG, MAN.   R3B 2E9
CANADA
Huygens' Principle   39

would have if the ground were perfectly conducting, i.e. if ϱ_A and ϱ_B were each equal to unity.

Substituting in eqn. (4.14) we have

$$Z_{ABO} = \frac{4K_2}{\sqrt{R_A R_B (R_A + R_B)}} \int_0^\infty \exp\left\{ -\frac{1}{2} j\beta_0 \left(\frac{1}{R_A} + \frac{1}{R_B} \right) z^2 \right\} dz$$

$$= \frac{j^{-1/2} 2 \sqrt{(2\pi)} K_2 \beta_0^{-1/2}}{R_A + R_B} \tag{4.19}$$

$$G = Z_{AB}/Z_{ABO} \simeq \frac{\sqrt{(\varepsilon_{rA} + 1)(\varepsilon_{rB} + 1)}}{j\beta_0 (R_A + R_B)} \tag{4.20}$$

In the case of a homogeneous earth ($\varepsilon_{rA} = \varepsilon_{rB}$) eqn. (4.20) agrees with Norton's (1936) result, showing that at great distances the groundwave fields are eventually attenuated according to an inverse-square law. The fact that the correct constant of proportionality is obtained using ray theory to compute the fields over the surface of integration supports the view that it is not helpful to think of the propagation as being by surface wave.

For the mixed-path problem illustrated in Fig. 4.8 eqn. (4.20) shows that provided the path over each type of ground is sufficiently long the attenuation factor is the geometric mean of the factors appropriate to the two types of ground (each in turn supposed to apply over the entire path). This result, derived differently by Feinberg (1945) and by Millington (1949), indicates that the ground has an influence only near the ends of the path.

Figure 4.9 shows an extension of the problem in which there is a discontinuity in the slope of the ground, as well as in the ground constants. For clarity the vertical scale of the figure has been exaggerated: the angles v_A and v_B are in fact assumed to be small in comparison with unity. On this assumption eqn. (4.17) requires modification only in respect of the exponential phase factor. The exponent is changed from

$$-\frac{1}{2} j\beta_0 \left(\frac{1}{R_A} + \frac{1}{R_B} \right) z^2$$

to

$$-\frac{1}{2} j\beta_0 \left(\frac{1}{R_A} + \frac{1}{R_B}\right)(z + z_0)^2$$

It is found that the effect of the discontinuity of slope is to multiply the attenuation factor G, which takes account of imperfect ground

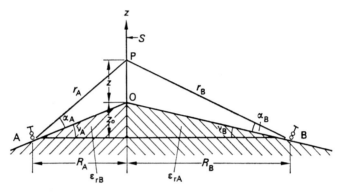

FIG. 4.9. Groundwave propagation over a ridge.

conductivity, by a further factor G_1, which takes account of the discontinuity of slope, so that the mutual impedance Z_{AB} is given by

$$Z_{AB} = GG_1 Z_{ABO} \tag{4.21}$$

G_1 is given by

$$G_1 = \frac{\displaystyle\int_0^\infty u^2 \exp\left\{-j(u + u_0)^2\right\} du}{\displaystyle\int_0^\infty u^2 \exp\left\{-ju^2\right\} du} \tag{4.22}$$

where

$$u_0^2 = \frac{1}{2} \beta_0 z_0^2 \left(\frac{1}{R_A} + \frac{1}{R_B}\right) = \frac{1}{2} \beta_0 (R_A + R_B) \gamma_A \gamma_B \tag{4.23}$$

G_1 may be evaluated as

$$G_1 = \frac{2}{\sqrt{\pi}} j^{-3/2} u_0 e^{-ju_0^2} + (1 + 2ju_0^2)\, \text{erfc}\,(u_0 \sqrt{j}) \tag{4.24}$$

where erfc (x), the error function complement, is given by

$$\text{erfc}\,(x) = \frac{2}{\sqrt{\pi}} \int_x^\infty e^{-t^2}\,dt \qquad (4.25)$$

For $u_0 \ll 1$ the first two terms in an expansion in powers of u_0 are given by

$$G \sim 1 + \frac{4}{\sqrt{\pi}}\,j^{-3/2}u_0 \qquad (4.26)$$

As might be expected the effect of the discontinuity is to retard the phase and reduce the magnitude of the field.

Equations (4.24) and (4.26) may also be applied when u_0 is negative, so that the ridge shown in Fig. 4.9 is replaced by a valley. The effect of the valley, when u is small and negative, is to advance the phase and increase the magnitude of the field.

For positive values of u_0 which are not small the validity of the original approximation—that fields over the surface of integration may be computed by ray theory—is doubtful however great the range.

4.5 Slots and Networks

It is instructive to consider two limiting cases in which the surface integral in eqn. (4.3) reduces firstly to a line integral and then to a series of discrete terms.

Suppose that the terminal-pairs A and B are completely separated by a conducting sheet in which is cut a slot, as shown in Fig. 4.10. If the slot is very narrow the electric field in its neighbourhood (Fig. 4.10b) will be effectively electrostatic, and may be defined in terms of a potential difference V varying along the length of the slot. If the surface S is taken to coincide with the conducting sheet the integrand will be zero except in the slot, and there the only significant contribution to the integral will be that associated with the predominant component of electric field: the component directed across the slot perpendicularly to its centre-line. It follows that the only component of magnetic field making a significant contribution to the integral will be parallel to the centre-line of the slot; this magnetic field will be associated with surface currents flowing in the sheet. Since perfect conductivity is assumed, skin effect will be complete and currents will flow independently on the two sides of the sheet.

The surface currents and the associated components of magnetic field may be resolved into symmetrical and asymmetrical components

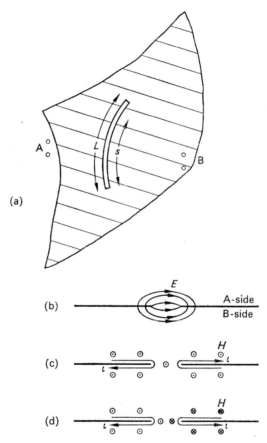

FIG. 4.10. Huygens' Principle for a slot. (a) A and B coupled through narrow slot. (b) Electric field in slot. (c) Surface current associated with symmetrical component of magnetic field. (d) Surface current associated with asymmetrical component of magnetic field.

as shown in Figs. 4.10(c) and (d), and it is clear that only the component shown in Fig. 4.10(c) will contribute to the integral. This component of surface current, when viewed from one side of the sheet only, appears to pass straight across the slot, although in fact it passes round each edge of the slot and flows in the opposite direction on the other side of the sheet.

If consideration is restricted to the predominant field components shown in Figs. 4.10(b) and (c), and if the fields are regarded as positive when they are directed as shown in these figures, eqn. (4.3) may be simplified to

$$Z_{AB} = \int_0^L ds \int_0^W (e_A h_B - e_B h_A) \, dw \qquad (4.27)$$

where w is distance from one edge of the slot and W is the total width.

Although the electric field will vary considerably in magnitude across the slot as shown in Fig. 4.10(b), the symmetrical component of magnetic field shown in Fig. 4.11(c) must be substantially uniform over the width if the slot is assumed to be narrow. This enables eqn. (4.27) to be further simplified to

$$Z_{AB} = \int_0^L (v_A h_B - v_B h_A) \, ds \qquad (4.28)$$

where $v_A(v_B)$ is the potential difference across the slot due to unit current injected between terminals A(B), terminals B(A) being open-circuit. In this equation h_A and h_B may be replaced by surface current densities (current per unit length of slot) ι_A and ι_B to give

$$Z_{AB} = \int_0^L (v_A \iota_B - v_B \iota_A) \, ds \qquad (4.29)$$

Equation (4.29) may have applications to slot aerials and to the coupling of waveguides by slots. It is also of interest as a bridge between eqn. (4.3) and the equivalent network theorem, which is applicable when the only significant contribution to the integral is made by field components that can be associated with well-defined currents in conductors passing through S and well-defined potential differences between those conductors.

It is convenient to begin by supposing that S coincides with a conducting sheet pierced with small holes through which pass wires, as shown in Fig. 4.11. These holes will be assumed to be so small that the current I_k carried by each wire where it passes through the hole, and the potential difference V_k between each wire and the conducting sheet, are well-defined quantities. (If this condition is not satisfied we are

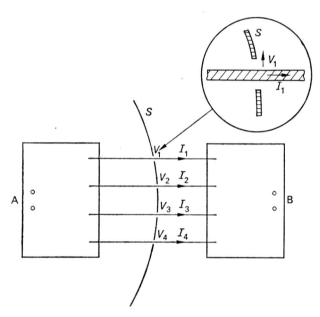

FIG. 4.11. Huygens' Principle for a circuit.

not entitled to think in terms of an electric circuit.) Under these conditions eqn. (4.3) becomes

$$Z_{AB} = \sum_k (v_{Ak} i_{Bk} - v_{Bk} i_{Ak}) \qquad (4.30)$$

where v_{Ak} and i_{Ak} are the values of V_k and I_k when unit current is impressed between terminals A, and similarly for v_{Bk} and i_{Bk}. This result may be deduced from eqn. (4.29) by treating the annular gap between each wire and the conducting sheet as a circular slot. Alternatively it may be deduced from eqn. (1.4) just as eqn. (4.3) was deduced from eqn. (2.9). It is not essential to postulate a conducting sheet with holes for the wires. It is sufficient to assume any configuration in which the only field components making a significant contribution to the integral in eqn. (4.8) are those which may be unambiguously associated with well-defined currents and potentials (potentials relative to any arbitrary datum).

4.6 *Rumsey's Reaction Concept*

This chapter would not be complete without some mention of the "reaction concept" introduced by Rumsey (1954).

Up to this point the only sources assumed have taken the form of currents impressed between pairs of terminals, and the coupling between terminal-pairs has been measured in terms of mutual impedance. This rather arbitrary method of description need usually involve no real loss of generality, since a pair of terminals may be regarded as those of an aerial or probe used either to excite or to measure fields; moreover the specialization resulting from consideration of terminal pairs does seem to aid physical understanding. Nevertheless, it is sometimes desirable to consider a more general type of source.

Rumsey was particularly concerned with an approximate analytical procedure, which was equivalent to a variational method but which could be interpreted in physical rather than purely mathematical terms. This procedure required the postulation of what might be termed a virtual source. For example, in order to determine the fields due to the scattering of waves by some conducting body the currents excited on the surface were regarded as a virtual source. The coupling between the virtual source and another source could not generally be described in terms of mutual impedance.

Consider two sources, denoted by the letters "a" and "b". Suppose that source a(b) takes the form of a volume distribution of impressed electric and magnetic current density $J_a(J_b)$ and $M_a(M_b)$, and that it excites electric and magnetic fields $E_a(E_b)$ and $H_a(H_b)$. The quantity $\langle a, b \rangle$ defined by

$$\langle a, b \rangle = \iiint (E_A \cdot J_B - H_A \cdot M_B)\, dv \qquad (4.31)$$

is termed the *reaction* between the sources a and b. The volume integral is taken over the entire region of space occupied by the sources. Equation (2.10) shows that

$$\langle a, b \rangle = \langle b, a \rangle \qquad (4.32)$$

In the special case where the sources a and b are unit electric currents impressed between pairs of terminals A and B, then

$$\langle a, b \rangle = -Z_{AB} \qquad (4.33)$$

where Z_{AB} is the mutual impedance between A and B.

Suppose that the sources a and b occupy separate regions of space so that it is possible to draw a closed surface S which entirely separates them. Then eqn. (2.8) leads to the result

$$\langle a, b \rangle = -\iint_S (E_A \times H_B - E_B \times H_A) \cdot \mathbf{n}\, dS \qquad (4.34)$$

where $\mathbf{n}$ is a unit vector normal to S and directed from b towards a. It follows from eqn. (4.33) that eqn. (4.34) may be regarded as a generalization of eqn. (4.3).

Note: For the sake of consistency within this monograph, Rumsey's notation has been changed. A current density J is here a vector equal in magnitude and phase to the current flowing across unit area of a surface normal to it. On the other hand, Rumsey's paper refers to a volume distribution of current dJ, where dJ is an elementary current moment, having the dimensions of current multiplied by distance.

Chapter 5

PERTURBATION METHODS

5.1 *Introductory*

Practical electromagnetic problems having an exact solution are in a minority; approximation is the essence of theoretical work. Approximations may be mathematical, when the physical situation is formulated exactly in mathematical terms and then solved approximately, or physical, when the problem is replaced by one that is approximately equivalent but which is susceptible of an exact solution. On the whole, physical approximations tend to be more fruitful because they are more easily guided by intuition and judgement. Moreover, a physical approximation may itself lead to useful conclusions additional to those arising from the solution itself.

Perturbation methods constitute one of the most useful types of physical approximation. The problem is changed to a simpler one having a known solution, and then this solution is modified to take account (approximately) of the effect of the change. The methods to be described in this chapter are all of this type, and may be thought of as generalizations of the compensation theorem, one of the elementary network theorems, which has been stated as follows:

If a network is altered by making a change ΔZ in the impedance Z of a branch, the change in the currents in all other branches is that which would be produced by an e.m.f. $-I\Delta Z$ acting in series with the modified branch, where I is the current in Z.

The dual of this statement is:

If a network is altered by making a change ΔY in the admittance Y of a branch, the change in the potential differences across all other branches is that which would be produced by impressing a current $-V\Delta Y$ in parallel with the modified branch where V is the potential difference across the unmodified branch.

It is proposed to consider an elementary application of this theorem in some detail because it provides a useful guide to the more general field theorems to be deduced later. The expression "Compensation Theorem" is often extended to cover these field theorems.

5.2 Network Theorem

It will be supposed that we require to know the effect of a change in each element of a two-port network upon the mutual impedance between its terminal pairs.

Figure 5.1 (Monteath, 1951) shows a network having pairs of terminals A, B, 1 ... k ... n, terminals 1 to n being connected to external impedances Z_1 to Z_n respectively. Let unit current applied to terminals A result in a current i_{Ak} in Z_k when terminals B are open-circuit, and let i_{Bk} be similarly defined. Let the mutual impedance between A and

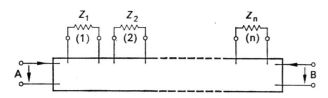

FIG. 5.1. Network theorem. (The arrows indicate the conventions adopted for positive currents and potential differences.)

B be Z_{AB}. Now suppose that the impedances $Z_1 \ldots Z_n$ are changed to $Z_1' \ldots Z_n'$, and that in consequence i_{Ak}, i_{Bk}, Z_{AB} change to i_{Ak}', i_{Bk}', Z_{AB}'. The change $Z_{AB}' - Z_{AB}$ in mutual impedance is equal to the sum of the potential differences between terminals B (both A and B being open-circuit) due to the operation of n generators having e.m.f.s typified by $-i_{Ak}(Z_k' - Z_k)$ operating in series with the impedances $Z_1' \dots Z_n'$.

Now it is often inconvenient to determine the effect of e.m.f.s operating in series with the elements of a network, whereas we have already assumed knowledge of the currents in the elements due to unit current injected between terminals A or B. It is therefore helpful to apply the reciprocity principle in the form of eqn. (2.16) and Fig. 2.3(c). This implies that the potential difference between terminals B, due to an e.m.f. V operating in series with Z_k' in the modified network, is equal to $-i_{Bk}'V$. It follows that

$$
\begin{aligned}
Z_{AB}' - Z_{AB} &= \sum_{k=1}^{n} i_{Ak} i_{Bk}' (Z_k' - Z_k) \\
&= \sum_{k=1}^{n} i_{Ak}' i_{Bk} (Z_k' - Z_k)
\end{aligned}
\Bigg\} \tag{5.1}
$$

Equations (5.1) are exact, but their utility lies in the fact that, if the quantities typified by $(Z_k' - Z_k)$ are sufficiently small i_{Ak}' will be approximately equal to i_{Ak}. Either equation may then be simplified to

$$
Z_{AB}' - Z_{AB} \simeq \sum_{k=1}^{n} i_{Ak} i_{Bk} (Z_k' - Z_k) \tag{5.2}
$$

The right-hand side may then be considered as the sum of the first-order terms in a Taylor series for Z_{AB}', regarding this as a function of the n variables $Z_1' \dots Z_n'$.

If it is required to calculate the effect of a small stray admittance in this way it is not practicable to think of a change in impedance from infinity to some large but finite value; it is therefore desirable to generalize the results to describe some of the elements in terms of admittance. Suppose that the circuit of Fig. 5.1 is modified by introducing m additional circuit elements characterized by admittances $Y_1 \dots Y_k \dots Y_m$ and that the potential difference across Y_k due to unit current injected between terminals A(B) is $v_{Ak}(v_{Bk})$. Now suppose that when the impedances $Z_1 \dots Z_k \dots Z_n$ change, the admittances $Y_1 \dots Y_k \dots Y_m$ change to $Y_1' \dots Y_k' \dots Y_m'$, while the potential differences across them change to v_{Ak}' and v_{Bk}', etc. The results corresponding to eqns. (5.1) and (5.2) are easily shown to be

$$Z'_{AB} - Z_{AB} = \sum_{k=1}^{n} i_{Ak} i'_{Bk} (Z'_k - Z_k) - \sum_{k=1}^{m} v_{Ak} v'_{Bk} (Y'_k - Y_k)$$

$$= \sum_{k=1}^{n} i'_{Ak} i_{Bk} (Z'_k - Z_k) - \sum_{k=1}^{m} v'_{Ak} v_{Bk} (Y'_k - Y_k) \qquad (5.3)$$

$$\simeq \sum_{k=1}^{n} i_{Ak} i_{Bk} (Z'_k - Z_k) - \sum_{k=1}^{m} v_{Ak} v_{Bk} (Y'_k - Y_k) \qquad (5.4)$$

These results apply to changes in discrete circuit elements, but they are not restricted to networks consisting *solely* of discrete elements.

Although either of the exact eqns. (5.3) leads to the same approximate result (5.4), it is sometimes easier to justify the approximation if one rather than the other exact equation is taken as a starting point. This is also true of the field theorems to be discussed later.

The effect of changes in the elements on the self-impedance may be determined by treating self-impedance as the mutual impedance between two pairs of terminals connected in parallel. Thus if Z_{AA} is the self-impedance at terminals A, either of the eqns. (5.3) gives

$$Z'_{AA} - Z_{AA} = \sum_{k=1}^{n} i_{Ak} i'_{Ak} (Z'_k - Z_k) - \sum_{k=1}^{m} v_{Ak} v'_{Ak} (Y'_k - Y_k) \qquad (5.5)$$

$$\simeq \sum_{k=1}^{n} i^2_{Ak} (Z'_k - Z_k) - \sum_{k=1}^{m} v^2_{Ak} (Y'_k - Y_k) \qquad (5.6)$$

In using eqns. (5.4) and (5.6) the decision whether to describe any particular circuit element in terms of impedance or admittance should be guided by whether it is the current through the element or the potential difference across it that can be regarded as approximately the same in the perturbed and unperturbed networks.

Equations (5.1)–(5.6) could be formulated in terms of characteristics of the network other than self- and mutual impedances, but this is not necessary since any multiport network may be described completely in terms of its impedance matrix, the elements of which are the self-impedances together with mutual impedances between terminal-pairs taken two at a time.

Equations (5.4) and (5.6) are useful for determining the tolerances required for the elements of a network, and for estimating the effect of dissipation in the elements, or of small stray inductances and capacitances, when it is difficult to take account of these exactly.

Equations (5.1) and (5.2) may sometimes be used to determine the effect of surface impedance.† A problem which can be tackled in this

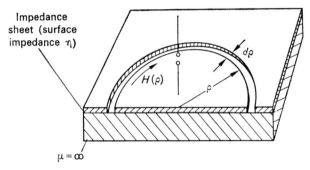

FIG. 5.2. Network theorem applied to surface impedance.

way concerns the effect of the finite surface impedance of the ground on the self-impedance of a vertical aerial. As shown in Fig. 5.2, the ground is regarded as a thin impedance sheet backed by some substance of infinite permeability, this sheet being divided into elementary annuli centred on the axis of the aerial. Each annulus (radii ϱ and $\varrho + d\varrho$) may be regarded as a network element of impedance $\eta \, d\varrho/2\pi\varrho$, where η is the surface impedance, carrying a current $2\pi\varrho H (\varrho)$, where $H(\varrho)$ is the magnetic field at the surface. If Z' is the input impedance of the aerial and Z is the value which it would have if the surface impedance of the ground were zero, eqns. (5.5) and (5.6) give

$$Z' - Z = 2\pi \int_0^\infty \eta h' (\varrho) \, h(\varrho) \, \varrho \, d\varrho \qquad (5.7)$$

$$\simeq 2\pi \int_0^\infty \eta h^2 (\varrho) \, \varrho \, d\varrho \qquad (5.8)$$

† The surface impedance concept will be discussed in Chapter 6.

where $h'(\varrho)$ is the magnetic field at the surface due to unit current impressed between the terminals of the aerial, and h is the value which h' would have if the ground were everywhere perfectly conducting. The replacement of eqn. (5.7) by eqn. (5.8) can be justified in most practical cases.

The simplicity of eqn. (5.8) and of its derivation suggest extensions of the method to more complex problems, but its applications are restricted by the need to treat elements of an impedance sheet as circuit elements. For example, it could not be applied in the absence of circular symmetry. A search for a less restricted method led to the more general results to be derived later.

Equation (5.4) or (5.6) may be applied to perturbation methods of measuring current, voltage or field. These methods, which were introduced by Cullen and Parr (1955), whose work will be referred to later, are particularly useful when the introduction of some kind of probe, with a connecting lead, would cause an undesirable disturbance of the system. For example, suppose that it is required to measure the relative amplitudes and phases of the voltages at the terminals of dipoles constituting an aerial array. The impedance may be measured at the input to the entire array while a small admittance is connected across each pair of terminals in turn. In some cases it may be sufficient to insert a piece of dielectric material between conductors already existing. The change in input impedance due to the connection of this admittance is proportional to the square of the voltage at the point of connection. Similarly a small impedance—for example, a toroidal magnetic core placed round an existing conductor—may be used to measure relative currents. Since the square of the voltage or current is measured there is an ambiguity of π in phase, but this can usually be resolved by other means.

Instead of impedance, admittance or any other analytic function of impedance may be measured. Only relative precision, not absolute accuracy, is required. Even so it is usually difficult to observe the small changes involved, but the arrangement shown in Fig. 5.3 eases this problem.

It is supposed that a number of elements—here shown as five

dipoles—are fed from some kind of power-dividing network, and that it is required to measure the relative voltage at the inputs to the dipoles, without disturbing the fields by the use of probes attached to leads. The aerial system is energized by an oscillator, the waves

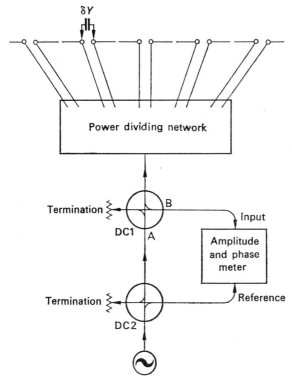

FIG. 5.3. Relative amplitude and phase measurement.

reflected in the feeder are sampled by a directional coupler DC1, and an amplitude and phase measurement is made by some suitable instrument. (A directional coupler is a matched four-port network such that the power entering it by any port divides between the paths indicated by the straight and curved lines.) For this purpose a reference signal from the same oscillator is required, and this may conveniently

3 AERP

be obtained from a second directional coupler DC2 sampling the forward wave in the feeder. The change (regarded as a complex quantity) in the measured amplitude and phase due to the connection of a small admittance δY is approximately proportional to the square of the voltage at the terminals to which it is applied.

There are two ways of justifying this procedure. In the first place the quantity being measured is an analytic function of the input impedance; therefore small changes in the measured quantity will, to a first order, be proportional to changes in the input impedance, so that eqn. (5.6) is applicable. Alternatively it may be supposed that the quantity being measured is the mutual impedance between terminal-pairs A and B of directional coupler DC1, so that eqn. (5.4) is applicable. These approaches lead to the same result, since the quantities i_{Ak} and i_{Bk} must be in a constant ratio, but the latter approach shows that no sacrifice of accuracy results from adopting the circuit of Fig. 5.3 instead of simply measuring input impedance. The advantage of this arrangement is an improvement in sensitivity, since by matching (at least approximately) the input to the power-dividing network (or by appropriately adjusting the load associated with DC1) the average amplitude of the input to the measuring device may be made small.

It is obviously desirable to make the admittance δY as large as it can be made without invalidating the approximation implicit in eqn. (5.4) or (5.6). Reference to eqn. (5.3) or (5.5) shows that we are actually measuring the geometric mean of the voltages across each terminal pair in the perturbed and unperturbed conditions. This observation leads to the conclusion that the error will be considerably reduced if a positive and negative susceptance are connected in turn to each point, so that the perturbation is a change in admittance from $Y - \frac{1}{2}\delta Y$ to $Y + \frac{1}{2}\delta Y$ instead of from Y to $Y + \delta Y$. Such a procedure may be convenient if there already exists at each point a variable shunt reactance (or series reactance if current is to be measured) which can be offset in either direction from its normal value.

Perturbation methods have been used more for measuring fields than for measuring current and voltage. Equations (5.4) or (5.6) may be applied to field measurement if the impedance which is to be perturbed is connected to an aerial placed at some point where the field is to be measured. It is, however, difficult to measure the minute changes in self- or mutual impedance which result, since these can easily be obscured by the effect of small mechanical changes due, for example, to change of temperature or vibration.

Cullen and Parr (1955), who were principally concerned with the measurement of electric field at microwave frequencies, overcame this

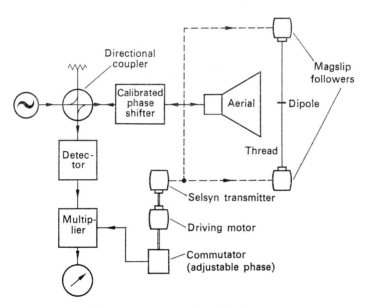

Fig. 5.4. Spinning-dipole method of field measurement.

difficulty by causing the perturbation to vary cyclically at about 30 Hz. Figure 5.4 illustrates the principle of their method, applied to measurement of the field in front of a horn aerial.

A small metal dipole is supported by a non-conducting thread, and is rotated at about 15 rev/sec by a pair of Magslip motors. The horn aerial is fed from a continuous-wave source through a hybrid device, shown as a directional coupler in the figure. Reflection due to re-radiation from the dipole, which will be modulated at twice the rotation frequency, is detected, and the alternating component of the output of the detector is rectified in a multiplier. The multiplier is supplied with a reference signal, a square-wave at twice the rotation frequency, generated by an adjustable commutator rotating in synchronism with the dipole.

The theory is derived in the original paper from the Lorentz reciprocity principle (eqn. 2.9) but it is sufficient here to outline the argument briefly. It is based on the assumption that the current in the dipole is approximately proportional to the electric field that would exist parallel to the dipole if the dipole were absent. This is equivalent to the approximation inherent in the use of eqn. (5.4) or (5.6) for current or voltage measurement. It implies that waves re-radiated by the dipole are not significantly reflected back to it by the aerial or by other neighbouring objects.

Let the component of electric field parallel to the dipole be E, and let the resulting current at the centre of the dipole be $K_1 E$, where K_1 is a complex constant. Let re-radiation by this current result in a signal W of complex amplitude $FK_1 E$ at the detector, where F must depend on the position of the dipole. Reciprocity shows that

$$F = K_2 E$$

where K_2 is a complex constant, so that

$$W = K_1 K_2 E^2 \qquad (5.9)$$

It follows that if W could be measured in amplitude and phase for each orientation of the dipole, the electric field (resolved parallel to the plane in which the dipole spins) would be determined, apart from a constant factor.

The r.f. phase of the received signal is determined as follows. The aerial is well matched, but the termination is deliberately mismatched so as to produce at the detector a steady component which predominates over all others. A small additional signal will influence the amplitude of the resultant only if it has a component in phase or in antiphase with the predominant signal. By setting the calibrated phase shifter in turn to two values differing by $\pi/4$, two quadrature components of the re-radiated signal may be determined separately.

One limitation of the method is that, since the square of the (complex) field is measured, there must be an ambiguity of π in phase, but this ambiguity can usually be resolved by other means. A more serious ambiguity arises from the fact that what is measured is the *variation* in the reflected signal as the dipole rotates. It may be shown that it is impossible to distinguish between a phase change of $\pi/2$ and a change of $\pi/2$ in the direction of the field.

Since the introduction of the spinning-dipole technique an alternative cyclical perturbation method of field measurement has been introduced by King (1965). A fixed dipole is connected to an impedance modulated at a low frequency: for example a photodiode illuminated by modulated light. This method enables the Cartesian components of the field to be measured separately. It may also have applications to current and voltage measurement.

5.3 *A Volume Integral Formula*

In this section an expression will be obtained for the effect of changes within a closed surface on the coupling between two terminal pairs outside the surface.

Figure 5.5 shows a closed surface S and two terminal-pairs, A and B, both outside S. It will be supposed that a sufficiently large volume including A, B and S is filled by a medium which is linear, isotropic and free from sources, apart from generators which may be connected

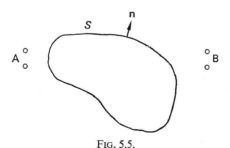

FIG. 5.5.

to A and B. This medium need not be uniform, and may therefore include conductors, some connected to the terminal pairs, which may pass through S. There will be obtained an expression for the change in the mutual impedance between A and B caused by changes, varying from point to point, of the permittivity and permeability of the medium

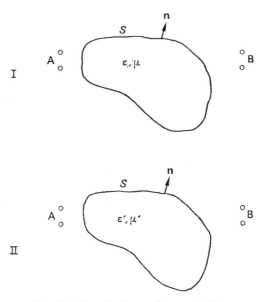

FIG. 5.6. Situation I: $e_A, h_A, e_B, h_B, Z_{AB}$;
Situation II: $e'_A, h'_A, e'_B, h'_B, Z'_{AB}$.

within S. This formulation is sufficiently general to include changes in the shape or position of conductors, dielectric bodies, etc.

Consider two situations, I and II, illustrated in Fig. 5.6.

Situation I. The permeability and permittivity (varying from point to point) are ε and μ respectively. Unit current injected between terminals A(B) (terminals B(A) being open-circuit) results in electric and magnetic fields e_A (e_B) and h_A (h_B) respectively. The mutual impedance between A and B is Z_{AB}.

Situation II. ε and μ are changed to ε' and μ', and in consequence

e_A, e_B, h_A, h_B and Z_{AB} are changed to e'_A, e'_B, h'_A, h'_B and Z'_{AB} respectively.

Suppose now that we begin with Situation I and inject unit current between terminals B. We may create exactly the same distribution of fields as in Situation II if we leave the permittivity and permeability (ε and μ) unchanged, but create by some means a distribution of impressed electric and magnetic current densities respectively equal to

$$j\omega e'_B (\varepsilon' - \varepsilon) \quad\text{and}\quad j\omega h'_B (\mu' - \mu)$$

In this situation the total current densities (impressed current together with displacement current) will be the same as in Situation II. It follows that the distribution of impressed electric and magnetic currents, operating in the unmodified medium (ε, μ), must result in a potential difference

$$Z'_{AB} - Z_{AB}$$

between terminals A when both terminal-pairs are open-circuit. All that remains is to determine this potential difference.

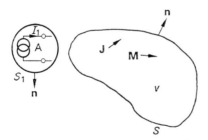

FIG. 5.7.

It is at this point that the reciprocity principle is used to determine the potential difference at a terminal-pair due to a volume distribution of impressed electric and magnetic currents.

Consider a non-uniform, but linear, passive and reciprocal medium which includes a pair of terminals A surrounded by a small closed surface S_1 as shown in Fig. 5.7. Two sources will be supposed to act:

Source 1: A current I_1 impressed between terminals A by a generator inside S_1, causing fields E_1 and H_1.

Source 2: A volume distribution of impressed electric and magnetic currents J and M respectively, contained within a volume v which is outside S_1 but is enclosed by a surface S. This sets up fields E_2, H_2, and results in an open-circuit potential difference V_2 (directed so as to oppose I_1) between terminals A.

Equation (2.11) is applied to S_1 and v giving

$$\iint_{S_1} (E_1 \times H_2 - E_2 \times H_1) \cdot \mathbf{n}\, dS = \iiint_v (E_1 \cdot J - H_1 \cdot M)\, dv$$

It is now supposed that S_1 is so small that eqn. (2.12) may be used to express the surface integral in terms of current and potential difference. Since the current generator within S_1 is assumed to have infinite impedance H_2 may be neglected on S_1. The result is

$$-V_2 I_1 = \iiint_v (E_1 \cdot J - H_1 \cdot M)\, dv \qquad (5.10)$$

In this equation we substitute

$$I_1 = 1$$
$$E_1 = e_A$$
$$H_1 = h_A$$
$$J = j\omega e'_B (\varepsilon' - \varepsilon)$$
$$M = j\omega h'_B (\mu' - \mu)$$
$$V_2 = Z'_{AB} - Z_{AB}$$

and obtain

$$Z'_{AB} - Z_{AB} = j\omega \iiint_v \{(\mu' - \mu) h_A \cdot h'_B - (\varepsilon' - \varepsilon) e_A \cdot e'_B\}\, dv \qquad (5.11)$$

This result (in which A and B may be interchanged) is a generalization of eqns. (5.3), the corresponding network formulae. Indeed, eqns. (5.3) could have been derived from eqn. (5.11) by supposing the changes in the elements of the network to result from changes in the complex permittivities and permeabilities of resistive material, dielectrics and magnetic cores.

If it is assumed that the effect of the changes in permittivity and permeability are insufficient to have much effect on the fields, the primes may be dropped on the right-hand side of eqn. (5.11) to give an approximate formula analogous to eqn. (5.4):

$$Z'_{AB} - Z_{AB} \simeq j\omega \iiint_v \{(\mu' - \mu) \boldsymbol{h}_A . \boldsymbol{h}_B - (\varepsilon' - \varepsilon) \boldsymbol{e}_A . \boldsymbol{e}_B\} \, dv \quad (5.12)$$

Results relating to self-impedance, analogous to eqns. (5.5) and (5.6), may readily be obtained by substituting A for B throughout. Care is, however, necessary in the interpretation of the scalar product of a vector with itself—for example, $\boldsymbol{e}_A . \boldsymbol{e}_A$. If $\boldsymbol{e}_A$ is linearly polarized the scalar product may be replaced by e_A^2, but this is not generally permissible. For example, if $\boldsymbol{e}_A$ possesses Cartesian components e_{Ax}, e_{Ay} and e_{Az}

$$\boldsymbol{e}_A . \boldsymbol{e}_A = e_{Ax}^2 + e_{Ay}^2 + e_{Az}^2 \quad (5.13)$$

but this equals e_A^2 only if the three components are co-phased, implying linear polarization. In other cases the scalar e_A has no meaning. In the extreme case in which $\boldsymbol{e}_A$ is circularly polarized $\boldsymbol{e}_A . \boldsymbol{e}_A$ is zero. (Verify by choosing axes so that e_{Ax} is real, e_{Ay} imaginary, and e_{Az} zero.)

One application of eqn. (5.12) is to reflections in a transmission line or waveguide due to a slight inhomogeneity of the dielectric. The treatment is similar to that of surface irregularity in section 7.1. As another example, eqn. (5.12) will be used to study the propagation of radio waves between two aerials as a result of scattering by atmospheric inhomogeneity caused by turbulence. This problem was originally solved by Booker and Gordon (1950).

Figure 5.8 shows two aerials operating at some high frequency (e.g. 1000 MHz) at which propagation by diffraction round the curve of the earth's surface is negligible. Unless ducts exist the aerials will be coupled together mainly by scattering due to the non-uniform permittivity of the atmosphere.

Suppose that the mutual impedance would be negligible in a uniform atmosphere and equal to Z'_{AB} in the presence of non-uniformity. Z'_{AB} is given by eqn. (5.11), which may be replaced by eqn. (5.12) without significant error; the approximation is equivalent to the neglect of multiple scattering. In fact the only regions of the atmosphere whose irregularity contributes significantly to the result are those

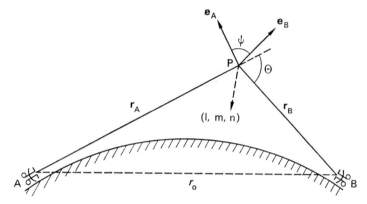

FIG. 5.8. Scattering by atmospheric inhomogeneity.

within optical range of both aerials, and in those regions the effect of scattering on the field strength will be negligible.

Taking account only of variations in permittivity, eqn. (5.12) becomes

$$Z'_{AB} \simeq -j\omega \iiint \delta\varepsilon \cdot e_A \cdot e_B \, dv \qquad (5.14)$$

writing $\delta\varepsilon = \varepsilon' - \varepsilon$ for the departure of the permittivity from its mean value. Now we may write

$$e_A = K_A F_A \frac{e^{-j\beta r_A}}{r_A} \qquad (5.15)$$

where K_A is a constant depending on the gain of aerial A, and F_A, which represents the radiation pattern of aerial A, is a function of the direction AP, and similarly for aerial B. It will be supposed that the maximum value of F_A and F_B is unity.

Equation (5.14) becomes

$$Z'_{AB} \simeq -j\omega K_A K_B \iiint \frac{\delta\varepsilon \, F_A F_B \, e^{-j\beta(r_A + r_B)} \cos\psi}{r_A r_B} \, dv \qquad (5.16)$$

where ψ is the angle between e_A and e_B. (Linear polarization is assumed for simplicity.) The integral is taken over all space contributing to the scattered field.

It is convenient to express this result in terms of a complex attenuation factor G, which is given by

$$G = Z'_{AB}/Z_{AB0}$$

Here Z_{AB0} is the mutual impedance that would exist if the aerials were arranged to point directly at one another, with the same polarization, in free space at a range r_0. Z_{AB0} may conveniently be derived from eqn. (4.3), taking S as the median plane separating the aerials. It is found that

$$Z_{AB0} = \frac{2K_A K_B \lambda}{j\eta r_0} \, e^{-j\beta r_0} \qquad (5.17)$$

where $\lambda = 2\pi/\beta$ and η are the wavelength and the intrinsic impedance† of the unperturbed atmosphere. Substituting for Z'_{AB} and Z_{AB0}

$$G = \frac{\omega\eta r_0}{2\lambda} \iiint \frac{\delta\varepsilon \cdot F_A F_B \cos\psi}{r_A r_B} \, e^{-j\beta(r_A + r_B - r_0)} \, dv \qquad (5.18)$$

Now G will be a quantity fluctuating with time in amplitude and phase; we require the mean-square value of its modulus. Taking Cartesian coordinates x, y, z along axes to be specified later $|G|^2$ is given by

$$|G|^2 = \frac{\omega^2 \eta^2 r_0^2}{4\lambda^2} \left[\iiint \frac{\delta\varepsilon \, F_A F_B \cos\psi}{r_A r_B} \, e^{-j\beta(r_A + r_B)} \, dx \, dy \, dz \right] \times$$

$$\times \left[\iiint \frac{\overset{*}{\delta\varepsilon} \, \overset{*}{F_A} \overset{*}{F_B} \cos\psi}{r_A r_B} \, e^{j\beta(r_A + r_B)} \, dx \, dy \, dz \right] \qquad (5.19)$$

† See Section 6.2.

where an asterisk denotes the complex conjugate. In the problem under consideration the imaginary part of $\delta\varepsilon$ will be negligible in practice, but the asterisk on it will nevertheless be retained for the sake of generality.

In the second triple integral the variables may be changed to x_1, y_1, z_1, and for the point (x_1, y_1, z_1) it will be supposed that $\delta\varepsilon, F_A, F_B, r_A, r_B$ and ψ become $\delta\varepsilon_1, F_{A1}, F_{B1}, r_{A1}, r_{B1}$ and ψ_1. The product of the two triple integrals may then be expressed as a sextuple integral:

$$|G|^2 = \frac{\omega^2\eta^2r_0^2}{4\lambda^2} \iiint\iiint \frac{\delta\varepsilon\,\delta\varepsilon_1\,F_A^*F_{A1}F_B^*F_{B1}\cos\psi\cos\psi_1}{r_A r_{A1} r_B r_{B1}} \times$$

$$\times\, e^{j\beta(r_{A1}+r_{B1}-r_A-r_B)}\,dx\,dy\,dz\,dx_1\,dy_1\,dz_1 \tag{5.20}$$

At this point it is necessary to make an approximation essential to the Booker–Gordon treatment. It will be supposed that the correlation between $\delta\varepsilon$ and $\delta\varepsilon_1$ is negligible unless the points (x, y, z) and (x_1, y_1, z_1) are so close together that

$$F_A \simeq F_{A1}$$

$$F_B \simeq F_{B1}$$

$$\cos\psi \simeq \cos\psi_1$$

$$1/r_A \simeq 1/r_{A1}$$

$$1/r_B \simeq 1/r_{B1}$$

although the exponential is still significant. Equation (5.20) may then be simplified as follows:

$$|G|^2 = \frac{\omega^2\eta^2r_0^2}{4\lambda^2} \iiint \frac{|F_A|^2\,|F_B|^2\cos^2\psi}{r_A^2 r_B^2} \times$$

$$\times \left\{ \iiint \delta\varepsilon\,\delta\varepsilon_1^*\, e^{j\beta(r_{A1}+r_{B1}-r_A-r_B)}\,dx_1\,dy_1\,dz_1 \right\} dx\,dy\,dz \tag{5.21}$$

The quantity required is $\overline{|G|^2}$, in which the bar denotes a mean with respect to time. This is obtained by replacing $\delta\varepsilon\delta\varepsilon_1^*$ by $\overline{\delta\varepsilon\delta\varepsilon_1^*}$. At the same time it is convenient to put

$$x_1 = x + u$$

$$y_1 = y + v$$

$$z_1 = z + w$$

Equation (5.21) becomes

$$\overline{|G|^2} = \frac{\omega^2\eta^2 r_0^2}{4\lambda^2} \iiint \frac{|F_A|^2 |F_B|^2 \cos^2\psi}{r_A^2 r_B^2} \times$$

$$\times \left\{ \iiint \overline{\delta\varepsilon\,\delta\varepsilon_1^*}\, e^{j\beta(r_{A1}+r_{B1}-r_A-r_B)}\, du\, dv\, dw \right\} dx\, dy\, dz \quad (5.22)$$

$\overline{\delta\varepsilon\delta\varepsilon_1^*}$, the autocorrelation function of $\delta\varepsilon$, will in general be a function of u, v and w, vanishing when any of these variables becomes sufficiently large. It will be a function of the single variable $(u^2 + v^2 + w^2)^{\frac{1}{2}}$ if the atmosphere is isotropic. This is normally assumed for the troposphere, although the assumption may be unjustified at greater distances, where the correlation tends to be least in the vertical direction.

Let Θ be the angle between AP and PB, that is the angle through which the incident radiation from A must be scattered to reach B (or vice-versa). Let the bisector of the angle APB have direction cosines (l, m, n) with the axes (x, y, z). Then since u, v and w are all assumed to be small in comparison with r_{A1}, etc., wherever $\overline{\delta\varepsilon\delta\varepsilon_1^*}$ is significant the exponent in eqn. (5.22) may be simplified by writing

$$r_{A1} + r_{B1} - r_A - r_B \simeq 2\,(lu + mv + nw)\sin\tfrac{1}{2}\Theta \quad (5.23)$$

Substituting in eqn. (5.22),

$$\overline{|G|^2} = \frac{\omega^2\eta^2 r_0^2}{4\lambda^2} \iiint \frac{|F_A|^2 |F_B|^2 \cos^2\psi}{r_A^2 r_B^2}\, S(\Theta)\, dx\, dy\, dz \quad (5.24)$$

where

$$S(\Theta) = \iiint \overline{\delta\varepsilon\,\delta\varepsilon_1^*}\; e^{2j\beta(lu+mv+nw)\sin\frac{1}{2}\Theta}\,du\,dv\,dw \qquad (5.25)$$

The integrals in eqn. (5.25) may be regarded as infinite because $\overline{\delta\varepsilon\delta\varepsilon_1^*}$ is assumed to vanish sufficiently rapidly at large enough values of any of the three components u, v and w of the vector $\overrightarrow{PP_1}$. Suppose now that the axes are rotated so as to change the variables to u', v' and w', where w' is aligned with the bisector of the angle APB (which has direction cosines (l, m, n) with respect to the old axes). Equation (5.25) becomes

$$S(\Theta) = \int_{-\infty}^{\infty}\int_{-\infty}^{\infty}\int_{-\infty}^{\infty} \overline{\delta\varepsilon\,\delta\varepsilon_1^*}\; e^{2j\beta w'\sin\frac{1}{2}\Theta}\,du'\,dv'\,dw' \qquad (5.26)$$

Here the integration with respect to u' and v' may be thought of as projecting the three-dimensional autocorrelation function $\overline{\delta\varepsilon\delta\varepsilon_1^*}$, a function of the three variables u', v', w', on to the w' axis so as to obtain a function of the single variable w'. $S(\Theta)$ is the Fourier transform of this function.

Further progress cannot be made without making some assumptions about $\overline{\delta\varepsilon\delta\varepsilon_1^*}$. Booker and Gordon assumed the troposphere to be statistically isotropic, and to have a real permittivity with an exponential autocorrelation function, so that

$$\overline{\delta\varepsilon\,\delta\varepsilon_1^*} = \overline{(\delta\varepsilon)^2}\; e^{-(u'^2+v'^2+w'^2)^{\frac{1}{2}}/d} \qquad (5.27)$$

where d is a length referred to as the "scale of turbulence". Substituting in eqn. (5.26) the integral may be evaluated to obtain

$$S(\Theta) = \frac{8\pi d^3\,\overline{(\delta\varepsilon)^2}}{(1+4\beta^2 d^2\sin^2\frac{1}{2}\Theta)^2} \qquad (5.28)$$

Substituting in eqn. (5.24),

$$\overline{|G|^2} = \frac{2\pi\omega^2\eta^2 r_0^2}{\lambda^2}\iiint \frac{|F_A|^2\,|F_B|^2 d^3\,\overline{(\delta\varepsilon)^2}\cos^2\psi}{r_A^2 r_B^2\,(1+4\beta^2 d^2\sin^2\frac{1}{2}\Theta)^2}\,dx\,dy\,dz \qquad (5.29)$$

Booker and Gordon give an expression for the power scattered by an elementary volume of the atmosphere towards the receiver. Their result agrees with eqn. (5.29) if ψ, which here represents the angle between the electric vectors associated with radiation from the two aerials, is replaced by $\pi/2 - X$. In Booker and Gordon's paper X represents the angle between the incident electric field and the direction in which the scattered radiation is observed. ψ and $\pi/2 - X$ are not the same, but there is here no conflict because eqn. (5.29) takes account only of that component of the scattered radiation which is polarized appropriately for the receiving aerial.

5.4 A Surface Integral Formula

The previous section considered changes in the permittivity and permeability of the medium throughout some finite volume. This approach is very general, but it is not conveniently applicable to changes in highly conducting bodies, in which the fields are confined to a shallow surface layer. In such problems it is better to use a surface integral. To this end the change $Z'_{AB} - Z_{AB}$ in the mutual impedance between the two terminal-pairs resulting from changes within some closed surface S will be expressed in terms of a surface integral over S.

One method of derivation follows the derivation of eqn. (5.11), but uses eqn. (2.9) (applied to both surfaces S_1 and S_2) instead of eqn. (2.11). Alternatively eqn. (5.11) may be taken as starting point and the volume integral transformed into a surface integral by methods used in Chapter 2. The result is

$$Z'_{AB} - Z_{AB} = \iint_S (e_A \times h'_B - e'_B \times h_A) \cdot \mathbf{n} \, dS \qquad (5.30)$$

where $\mathbf{n}$ is a unit vector in the direction of the outward normal as shown in Fig. 5.5 (Monteath, 1951). As before, self-impedance may be treated as mutual impedance between coincident terminals, giving

$$Z'_{AA} - Z_{AA} = \iint_S (e_A \times h'_A - e'_A \times h_A) \cdot \mathbf{n} \, dS \qquad (5.31)$$

These results have some affinity with Huygens' Principle, which expresses the effect of a distribution of sources by an integral over a closed surface surrounding them.

Equation (5.31), often referred to as "the compensation theorem for fields", has been a fruitful source of solutions to a number of problems, particularly those concerned with radiation and propagation of radio waves from aerials near to the ground. Its use is closely allied to earlier procedures using Green's Theorem, which will be discussed in Chapter 9. Most applications involve the concept of surface impedance, which will be discussed in the next chapter.

Chapter 6

SURFACE IMPEDANCE

6.1 *General*

ALTHOUGH the impedance concept is not essential to the reciprocity principle it plays an important part in many of its applications. In network analysis, impedance expresses a relationship between current and potential difference, but Schelkunoff (1938) and others have generalized this concept so as to relate electric and magnetic fields in space. Thus, if the components of electric and magnetic field tangential to a surface S at some point are perpendicular, then the ratio of the tangential electric field to the tangential magnetic field is termed *the field impedance normal to S*. In general the electric and magnetic fields are not perpendicular, so that the field impedance does not exist (just as the derivative of a function of a complex variable is said not to exist if the function fails to satisfy the Cauchy–Riemann equations). Even when the field impedance does exist, it will in general depend on the configuration of sources by which the fields have been set up. However, it will be shown that under certain conditions the field impedance normal to a boundary between two media does exist and is substantially independent of the sources. It is then reasonable to regard it as an intrinsic property of the boundary, and to term it the *surface impedance*.

A boundary surface exhibiting a well-defined surface impedance η behaves like an impedance sheet—a thin film having an impedance η measured between opposite sides of any small square—backed by some substance of infinite permeability. The surface impedance is analogous to the impedance of a load terminating a transmission line. Some authors also apply the term to an impedance sheet, such as a grating; this is analogous to an impedance connected across a transmission line at some point in its length.

6.2 *The Plane Surface of a Semi-infinite Homogeneous Medium*

In Fig. 6.1 (Monteath, 1951) the xy-plane is the boundary between two semi-infinite homogeneous media; it will be assumed that sources exist in the upper medium. Suppose that in the first place these sources set up uniform plane waves travelling along the z-axis. It follows immediately from Maxwell's equations that the electric field components E_x, E_y are determined by the magnetic field components H_x, H_y as follows:

$$E_x = \eta H_y \tag{6.1}$$

$$E_y = -\eta H_x$$

where

$$\eta = \sqrt{(\mu/\varepsilon)} \tag{6.2}$$

The quantity η is termed the *intrinsic impedance* of the medium. In rationalized m.k.s. units the intrinsic impedance of free space is equal to 377 ohms.

To state that the fields are associated with uniform plane waves

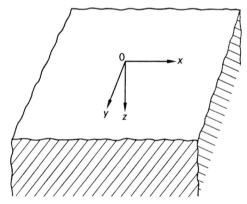

FIG. 6.1. Surface impedance of a semi-infinite medium.

normally incident is tantamount to saying that the tangential magnetic field is uniform over the whole xy plane. It is therefore reasonable to expect that eqns. (6.1) will be satisfied at least approximately if H_x and H_y vary sufficiently slowly with x and y. Now the only standard of length by which we can judge the rate of variation of H_x and H_y is $|\beta|^{-1}$ where $j\beta = j\omega \sqrt{(\mu\varepsilon)}$ is termed the *intrinsic propagation constant* of the medium (the lower medium in Fig. 6.1). This intuitive argument can be placed on a sounder basis as follows:

Let the magnetic field components in the lower medium ($z > 0$) be expressed as an angular spectrum of plane waves (Clemmow, 1966) as follows:

$$
\left.
\begin{aligned}
H_x &= \int_{-\infty}^{\infty} \int_{-\infty}^{\infty} \phi_x (\beta_x, \beta_y)\, e^{-j(\beta_x x + \beta_y y + \beta_z z)}\, d\beta_x\, d\beta_y \\
H_y &= \int_{-\infty}^{\infty} \int_{-\infty}^{\infty} \phi_y (\beta_x, \beta_y)\, e^{-j(\beta_x x + \beta_y y + \beta_z z)}\, d\beta_x\, d\beta_y
\end{aligned}
\right\}
\tag{6.3}
$$

where $j\beta_x$, etc., are components of the propagation constant resolved along the axes. These satisfy the relation

$$
\beta_x^2 + \beta_y^2 + \beta_z^2 = \beta^2
\tag{6.4}
$$

where $j\beta = j\omega \sqrt{(\mu\varepsilon)}$ is the intrinsic propagation constant of the lower medium. The fact that all sources are assumed to be in the region ($z < 0$) implies that for $z > 0$ all component waves are propagated in the positive-z direction. It follows that if β_z is determined from eqn. (6.4) the root falling in the first quadrant should be chosen.

H_z may be deduced from eqns. (6.3) by the use of Poisson's equation (div $\mathbf{H} = 0$), and E_x and E_y may then be determined from

$$
j\omega\varepsilon\mathbf{E} = \operatorname{curl} \mathbf{H}
$$

It is found that

$$
E_x = \eta \int_{-\infty}^{\infty} \int_{-\infty}^{\infty} \frac{\dfrac{\beta_x \beta_y}{\beta^2} \phi_x + \left(1 - \dfrac{\beta_x^2}{\beta^2}\right) \phi_y}{\sqrt{1 - (\beta_x^2 + \beta_y^2)/\beta^2}} \cdot e^{-j(\beta_x x + \beta_y y + \beta_z z)}\, d\beta_x\, d\beta_y
\tag{6.5}
$$

and similarly for E_y.

If the question of convergence is set on one side, the factor $[1 - (\beta_x^2 + \beta_y^2)/\beta^2]^{-1/2}$ may be expanded in a power series. It is then permissible to replace β_x by $j\,(\partial/\partial x)$ etc., and by using eqns. (6.3), E_x and E_y may be expressed in terms of H_x, H_y, and their derivatives with respect to x and y as follows (Monteath, 1951):

$$\left.\begin{aligned} E_x &= \eta H_y + \frac{\eta}{2\beta^2}\left[\left(\frac{\partial^2}{\partial x^2} - \frac{\partial^2}{\partial y^2}\right)H_y - 2\frac{\partial^2}{\partial x\,\partial y}H_x\right] \\ &\quad + \text{terms in } \beta^{-4}\text{ etc.} \\ E_y &= -\eta H_x + \frac{\eta}{2\beta^2}\left[\left(\frac{\partial^2}{\partial x^2} - \frac{\partial^2}{\partial y^2}\right)H_x + 2\frac{\partial^2}{\partial x\,\partial y}H_y\right] \\ &\quad + \text{terms in } \beta^{-4}\text{ etc.} \end{aligned}\right\} \quad (6.6)$$

The series expansion of eqn. (6.5) diverges for $|\beta_x^2 + \beta_y^2| > \beta^2$ but it is reasonable to regard eqns. (6.6) as asymptotic expansions in inverse powers of β. If the second term in each of eqns. (6.6) is sufficiently small these equations may be replaced by eqns. (6.1); only under these conditions is the concept of surface impedance truly valid. It is found to be entirely valid when applied to the effect of finite conductivity in metals at radio frequencies, unless very sharp edges are involved, because conduction gives ε an enormous (imaginary) value, so that β^2 is very large. The validity of its application to the propagation of radio waves over the earth has been reviewed very thoroughly by Godziński (1961) to whose paper the reader is referred for a survey of the literature.

In many problems presented by the propagation of radio waves over the earth the fields at the surface approximate to those associated with uniform plane waves at grazing incidence rather than at normal incidence. In these cases is may be shown that better approximations than eqns. (6.1) are

$$\left.\begin{aligned} E_x &\simeq \eta\left(1 - \frac{\varepsilon_0}{\varepsilon}\right)H_y \simeq \sqrt{\frac{\mu}{\varepsilon + \varepsilon_0}}\,H_y \\ E_y &\simeq -\eta\left(1 - \frac{\varepsilon_0}{\varepsilon}\right)H_x \simeq -\sqrt{\frac{\mu}{\varepsilon + \varepsilon_0}}\,H_x \end{aligned}\right\} \quad (6.7)$$

for vertical polarization ($H_z = 0$) and

$$E_x \simeq \eta \left(1 + \frac{\varepsilon_0}{\varepsilon}\right) H_y \simeq \sqrt{\frac{\mu}{\varepsilon - \varepsilon_0}} \, H_y$$

$$E_y \simeq -\eta \left(1 + \frac{\varepsilon}{\varepsilon_0}\right) H_x \simeq -\sqrt{\frac{\mu}{\varepsilon - \varepsilon_0}} \, H_x$$

$$\tag{6.8}$$

for horizontal polarization ($E_z = 0$).

These results are correct to the first order in $\varepsilon_0/\varepsilon$, incorporating the terms proportional to β^{-2} in eqns. (6.6). The correction implicit in the use of eqns. (6.7) or (6.8) rather than eqns. (6.1) is equivalent to a change of unity in the complex relative permittivity of the ground. It is usually unimportant.

6.3 Inhomogeneous Media

Although the foregoing discussion was concerned with the plane surface of a semi-infinite homogeneous medium, the surface impedance concept is particularly valuable in a number of less simple cases, where any other approach would be impracticable. Some of these cases are outlined briefly below.

When the medium is composed of a number of layers parallel to the surface it is permissible to assign a surface impedance to the outer surface, provided that every material to which the waves can penetrate has a sufficiently large propagation constant. The surface impedance may be computed with sufficient accuracy by supposing uniform plane waves to be incident normally; as pointed out by Schelkunoff (1938), this procedure is analogous to the use of transmission line theory. Stratified ground has been studied in detail by Wait (1954).

Curvature of the boundary surface may be neglected provided that the radius of curvature is large compared with the reciprocal of the propagation constant.

Variation in the properties of the medium in directions parallel to the surface can be taken into account by regarding the surface impedance as a function of position, but in general the rate of variation must be small, as usual taking the reciprocal of the propagation coefficient as the standard of length. Relaxation of this restriction can be justified in certain special cases; one of these, involving circular symmetry, is illustrated in Fig. 6.2.

A vertical aerial is energized by a generator connected between its lower end and a long vertical cylinder embedded in the ground. It will

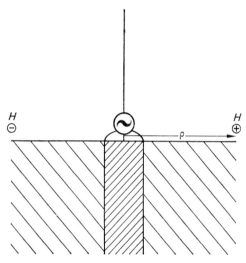

H
$\ominus$

H
$\oplus$

ρ

FIG. 6.2. Cylindrical earth system.

be assumed that this cylinder is long in comparison with the skin depth $1/\mathrm{Im}\,(\beta)$. At the surface of the ground the magnetic field H will be horizontal, and near the axis of symmetry it will vary very rapidly from point to point (tending to infinity as the radius ϱ tends to zero). However, if the product ϱH were independent of ϱ the fields would correspond to transverse electromagnetic waves, such as those in a coaxial transmission line, and it may be shown that for such waves eqns. (6.1) are exact. Now although ϱH is not constant, it will in many cases vary quite slowly with ϱ: the scale-factor determining this rate of variation is either $1/\beta_0 = \lambda/2\pi$ or the height of the aerial, whichever is the smaller. Provided that both these quantities are large compared with $1/\beta$ it is reasonable to suppose that these eqns. (6.1) are satisfied approximately. This intuitive supposition can be justified by reformulating eqns. (6.6) in cylindrical polar coordinates. The quantity $2\pi\varrho H$ may be identified with the total surface current crossing a circle of radius ϱ.

Figure 6.3 illustrates another situation requiring special consideration. A thin perfectly conducting sheet, which for simplicity will be assumed to be semi-infinite with a straight edge, is laid upon the surface of the ground, and it is supposed that a uniform horizontal magnetic field H_0, parallel to the edge, is impressed on the upper surface of the sheet and on the exposed surface of the ground. Now in the interface between the sheet and the ground the magnetic field must vary quite rapidly near to the edge of the sheet, for it must

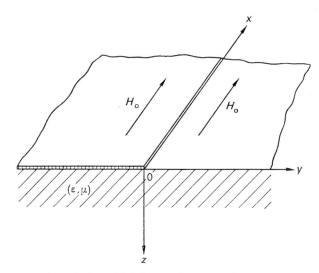

FIG. 6.3. A semi-infinite metal sheet on the ground.

become zero at points well away (in comparison with $1/|\beta|$) from the edge; it follows that the conditions for eqns. (6.1) are not satisfied. An alternative view is that the current flowing in the sheet must leave it near the edge and spread out into the ground; within the region in which the spreading-out takes place the current density will be great, and the horizontal electric field will be greater than it would be if the conducting sheet were absent. The resulting error may be assessed by the method outlined below.

The magnetic field H_x in the ground ($z > 0$) may be expressed in terms of an angular spectrum of plane waves thus:

$$H_x = \int_C f(\beta_y) \, e^{-j(\beta_y y + \beta_z z)} \, d\beta_y \tag{6.9}$$

where

$$\beta_y^2 + \beta_z^2 = \beta^2 = \omega^2 \mu \varepsilon \tag{6.10}$$

The contour C must pass from $-\infty$ to ∞. The integrand will have branch points at $\pm\beta$; if the medium is lossy these will be displaced

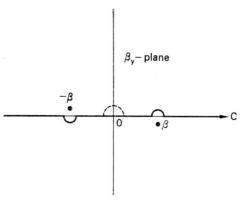

FIG. 6.4. Contour C.

from the real axis as shown in Fig. 6.4. If the material is lossless, so that β is real, the contour must be indented as shown to ensure that the real part of β_z is always positive, so that within the ground all component plane waves are propagated downwards rather than upwards. Using Maxwell's equations the component of electric field parallel to the surface is found to be

$$E_y = -\eta \int_C f(\beta_y) \frac{\beta_z}{\beta} \, e^{-j(\beta_y y + \beta_z z)} \, d\beta_y \tag{6.11}$$

Now in the interface between the ground and the metal sheet E_y must be zero, although H_x is unknown; while on the exposed surface of the ground H_x has been assumed to be equal to H_0, although E_y is unknown. Thus for $z = 0$,

$$H_x = \int_C f(\beta_y) \, e^{-\beta_y y} \, d\beta_y = H_0 \qquad (6.12)$$

$(y > 0)$

$$E_y = -\frac{\eta}{\beta} \int_C f(\beta_y) \sqrt{\beta^2 - \beta_y^2} \, e^{-j\beta_y y} \, d\beta_y = 0 \qquad (6.13)$$

$(y < 0)$

There is a well-known technique for solving such a pair of dual integral equations. In eqn. (6.12) the contour may be closed by an infinite semicircle in the lower half of the plane; the only singularity of $f(\beta_y)$ then enclosed must be a pole with the appropriate residue. In eqn. (6.13) the contour may be closed in the lower half-plane; no singularity of $f(\beta_y) \sqrt{\beta^2 - \beta_y^2}$ must then be enclosed, so that the branch-point at β must be cancelled out. These conditions lead to the result:

$$f(\beta_y) = -\frac{H_0 \sqrt{\beta}}{2\pi j \beta_y \sqrt{\beta + \beta_y}} \qquad (6.14)$$

with the contour indented at the origin as shown by the broken line. Substitution in eqn. (6.13) leads to an integral expression for E_y. Applying this to the surface of the ground not covered by the sheet it is found that

$$E_y = -\eta H_0 - \Delta E \qquad (6.15)$$

where

$$\Delta E = \frac{\eta H_0}{\pi} \int_\beta^\infty \frac{\sqrt{t/\beta - 1}}{t} \, e^{-jty} \, dt \qquad (6.16)$$

$(y > 0; z = 0)$

ΔE is small for $\beta y \gg 1$; if β is sufficiently large it may be neglected for most purposes. A better approximation is obtained by determining the quantity ΔV, given by

$$\Delta V = \int_0^\infty \Delta E \, dy \qquad (6.17)$$

and replacing ΔE by an impulse of strength ΔV at $y = 0+$. By substituting for ΔE from eqn. (6.16) in eqn. (6.17), and reversing the order of integration, it is found that

$$\Delta V = \frac{\eta H_o}{2j\beta} \qquad (6.18)$$

This result implies that the discontinuity at the edge of the sheet has the effect of augmenting the surface impedance by a *line impedance* $\mathscr{Z}$ (dimensions resistance × length) at the edge, where

$$\mathscr{Z} = \eta/2j\beta \qquad (6.19)$$

The last example of a situation in which the surface impedance concept requires special consideration is illustrated in Fig. 6.5. A grid of parallel wires, perpendicular to the magnetic field, is laid upon the surface of the ground.

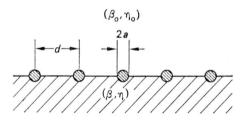

FIG. 6.5. Wire grating in an interface.

In an infinite homogeneous medium an infinite plane grating of thin closely spaced parallel wires behaves like a reactive impedance sheet. Its impedance η_w is given by the following well-known formula:

$$\eta_\omega = \frac{j\eta\beta d}{2\pi} \log \frac{d}{2\pi a} \qquad (6.20)$$

where d is the spacing between the wires, a the wire radius, and jβ and η the propagation constant and intrinsic impedance of the medium. This result is not exact, but is a good approximation if the following conditions are satisfied:

(i) $d \gg 2\pi a$

(ii) $\beta d \ll 1$

(iii) The fields are not examined so near to the plane of the grating that components varying periodically from wire to wire are significant.

(iv) The incident magnetic field does not vary too rapidly from point to point of the grating. The standard of length by which this variation is to be judged is d.

The more complex situation of Fig. 6.5 may be studied in the following way. Regarding the fields as set up by an angular spectrum of plane waves incident from above, one typical plane-wave component of this spectrum is considered alone. It is then assumed that in response to excitation by the single component, currents in the grating set up an angular spectrum of plane waves propagated upwards and downwards from the interface. This spectrum is determined by satisfying the appropriate boundary conditions at the interface between the ground and the air and at the surface of the wires. It is then found that if d is sufficiently small the fields above ground at points not too close to the grating can be expressed in terms of the incident waves and waves reflected by the surface. The reflection coefficient at the surface is obtained by combining the impedance of the grating, given by eqn. (6.20), and the surface impedance of the ground as impedances in parallel. This simple result is sufficiently accurate for most purposes provided that $d < 1/|\beta|$. In practice it is found that where this condition is not satisfied the grating has not much effect anyway. A more accurate solution has been published by Wait (1957a).

The condition for assigning a surface impedance η to the ground alone (that the incident fields do not vary much in a distance $1/|\beta|$) is of course still applicable.

6.4 *Application of Surface Impedance to Perturbation Methods*

Equation (5.30) expressed a change in mutual impedance due to changes within a closed surface S in terms of a surface integral over S. Suppose now that S is a boundary surface to which a surface impedance can be assigned, and that the change to be considered is simply a change in that surface impedance from η to η'. (In general both η and η' may vary from point to point.) Bearing in mind that only field components tangential to S contribute to eqn. (5.30) it is found that

$$\left. \begin{aligned} (e_A \times h'_B) \cdot \mathbf{n} &= -\eta h_{At} \cdot h'_{Bt} \\ (e'_B \times h_A) \cdot \mathbf{n} &= -\eta' h'_{Bt} \cdot h_{At} \end{aligned} \right\} \qquad (6.21)$$

where $\mathbf{n}$ is a unit vector in the direction of the outward normal and the subscript t implies the tangential component. Equation (5.30) becomes (Monteath, 1951)

$$Z'_{AB} - Z_{AB} = \iint_S (\eta' - \eta)\, h_{At} \cdot h'_{Bt}\, dS \qquad (6.22)$$

This result has been termed the *compensation theorem for a boundary surface*. Like eqn. (5.30) it has been used in many published papers to solve aerial and propagation problems.

Equation (6.22) is really a specialization of eqn. (5.11), which gave the effect of changes in the bulk properties of a medium, expressed in terms of permeability and permittivity. It is instructive to take this specialization further by considering a system of imperfectly conducting wires. These will be supposed so thin that the circumferential magnetic field at the surface of a wire can be expressed in terms of a longitudinal current. The ratio $\varkappa$ of the longitudinal electric field at the surface of a wire to the longitudinal current, which is sometimes referred to as the *internal impedance* per unit length, is given by

$$\varkappa = \eta/2\pi a \qquad (6.23)$$

where a is the radius.

Applying eqn. (6.22) to the surface of the wire, and writing $i_A = 2\pi a h_{At}$ for the longitudinal current due to unit current impressed between terminals A, gives

$$Z'_{AB} - Z_{AB} = \int (z' - z) i_A i'_B \, ds \qquad (6.24)$$

where the integral is taken along the length of the wire. This result may be used to determine the effect of finite internal impedance on the performance of an aerial system composed of wires.

Chapter 7

APPLICATIONS OF SURFACE INTEGRAL PERTURBATION FORMULAE

7.1 *Waveguides*

Equation (6.22), which gives the effect of a change in surface impedance, has many applications, including the effect of finite conductivity on the properties of transmission lines, waveguides and cavities. As

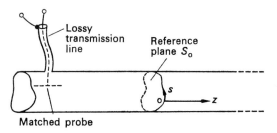

FIG. 7.1. Reflection due to the non-uniform surface impedance of a waveguide.

an example Fig. 7.1 represents a semi-infinite waveguide of uniform but arbitrary cross-section energized by some kind of probe connected to a terminal pair. Equation (6.22) will be used to investigate the reflections resulting from non-uniformity of the surface impedance.

A reference plane S_0, normal to the generators of the waveguide, will be taken through a point 0 on the surface. It will be assumed that at the frequency of operation the guide can support only one mode and that S_0, and the region of varying surface impedance, are sufficiently remote from the input probe for evanescent modes originating there to be negligible. It will also be assumed—although this assumption entails no real loss of generality—that considerable attenuation exists in the transmission line between the probe and the input terminals, and that the probe is arranged to match the waveguide, so that waves reflected back towards the input are absorbed without reflection, whatever the conditions at the input terminals.

A point on the (inner) surface of the guide will be defined by coordinates (z, s), where the axis $0z$ is a generator of the guide and the coordinate s is measured from 0 round the perimeter of S_0.

Suppose in the first place that the surface impedance is equal to a constant η and that in this condition the waveguide is perfectly matched. Let the fields due to unit current impressed between the terminals be e and h and let the input impedance be Z. Now let the surface impedance for $z > 0$ change to η' (an arbitrary function of s and z) and let e, h and Z change to e', h' and Z'. Equation (6.22) gives

$$Z' - Z = \int_0^\infty dz \oint_s h_t \cdot h_t' \, (\eta' - \eta) \, ds \qquad (7.1)$$

where the subscript t denotes the component tangential to the surface. It will now be assumed that η and η' are sufficiently small to have only a small effect on the distribution of the fields over the cross-section, and that the reflections under investigation are sufficiently slight for multiple reflections to be ignored. We may therefore write:

$$h_t' \simeq h_t \qquad (7.2)$$

It is also permissible to replace h_t by h because h must be almost exactly tangential to the surface of the waveguide. Equation (7.1) becomes:

$$Z' - Z \simeq \int_0^\infty dz \oint_s h \cdot h \, (\eta' - \eta) \, ds \qquad (7.3)$$

Now suppose that the waveguide is terminated by means of a perfectly conducting partition in the reference plane. In this case the reflection coefficient, regarding the waves as represented by the transverse component of electric field, is equal to -1. Let the input impedance in this condition be Z'' and let the fields for unit input current be e'' and h''. Then eqn. (5.31) gives:

$$Z'' - Z = -\iint_{S_0} (e \times h'' - e'' \times h) . k \, dS$$

where k is a unit vector in the $+z$ direction. Now, since the partition is perfectly conducting, the transverse component of e'' will be zero. Moreover, the transverse component of h'' will be equal to twice that of h. It follows that

$$Z'' - Z = -2\iint_{S_0} e \times h . k \, dS \tag{7.4}$$

Now since it has been assumed that there is considerable attenuation in the input transmission line $Z' - Z$, $Z'' - Z$ and reflection coefficients observed at the input terminals will all be small. It follows that impedance changes are directly proportional to the corresponding reflection coefficients. Since $Z'' - Z$ corresponds to a reflection coefficient of -1 referred to the origin, eqns. (7.3) and (7.4) enable the reflection coefficient ϱ due to the impedance irregularities to be referred to the origin also. The result is

$$\varrho = \frac{\displaystyle\int_0^\infty dz \oint_s h . h (\eta' - \eta) \, ds}{2\displaystyle\iint_{S_0} e \times h . k \, dS} \tag{7.5}$$

The integral in the numerator is taken over the wall of the waveguide. That in the denominator is taken over any cross-section to which the reflection coefficient is to be referred.

It must be emphasized that the scalar product $h . h$ in eqn. (7.5) may not be replaced by h^2 unless h is linearly polarized. If, as will generally be true, it is elliptically polarized, orthogonal components in phase quadrature will make contributions of opposite sign to $h . h$. For example, wherever h is circularly polarized the surface impedance will have no first-order effect on the reflection coefficient.

Reflections caused by discontinuities in the surface impedance of a waveguide can almost always be neglected in practice, but it is sometimes necessary to examine them in connection with impedance measurements of the highest precision.

More important are the reflections caused by small irregularities in the shape of a waveguide. Figure 7.2 shows a waveguide which is perfectly conducting and uniform apart from a shallow dent which has deformed a portion T of the surface into T'. Equation (5.31) will

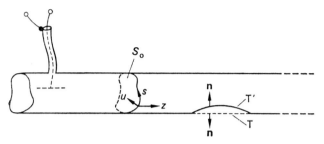

FIG. 7.2. Reflection by a dent in a waveguide.

be used to determine the effect of the dent on the input impedance. This is given by

$$Z' - Z = \iint_{T+T'} (e \times h' - e' \times h) \cdot n \, dS \qquad (7.6)$$

where e and h represent the electric and magnetic fields for unit input current when the waveguide is not deformed and e' and h' are the corresponding components in the presence of the dent.

Now e' is zero over T, and its tangential component is zero over T', so that eqn. (7.6) may be simplified to

$$Z' - Z = \iint_{T+T'} e \times h' \cdot n \, dS \qquad (7.7)$$

(T does not contribute to the integral, but it is convenient to retain the whole of the closed surface.) It will be supposed that the dent is shallow, so that we are concerned with fields only in a region close to the undeformed surface of the guide. Under these conditions it is permissible to adopt the coordinates (z, s, u) illustrated in Fig. 7.2,

4 AERP

which will be approximately orthogonal in this region. As before z is measured along a generator and s along the perimeter of a normal cross-section of the undeformed waveguide. The coordinate u is measured normally inwards from the undeformed surface. The surface T' may then be defined by

$$u = \xi f(s, z)$$

where ξ is a constant scale factor. The reflection coefficient will be a function of ξ and might be expanded in a power series; we shall consider only the term proportional to ξ.

Now the tangential component of e over T' will tend to zero with ξ and it is not difficult to see that it must do so as rapidly as ξ. Moreover, h' will tend to h as ξ tends to zero. It follows that since the result is required only to the first order in ξ, h' may be replaced by h in eqn. (7.7), which becomes

$$Z' - Z \simeq \iint_{T+T'} e \times h \cdot n \, dS \qquad (7.8)$$

Using the divergence theorem, together with eqns. (2.5), (2.1) and (2.2), eqn. (7.8) may be transformed into an integral over the volume v that has been excluded from the interior of the waveguide by the dent:

$$Z' - Z \simeq -j\omega \iiint_{v} (\varepsilon e \cdot e + \mu h \cdot h) \, dv \qquad (7.9)$$

Since the solution will be correct only to the first order in ξ, e and h may be assigned their values at the undeformed waveguide surface, giving

$$Z' - Z \simeq -j\omega\xi \int_{0}^{\infty} dz \oint_{s} (\varepsilon e^2 + \mu h \cdot h)_{u=0} f(s, z) \, ds \qquad (7.10)$$

(Note that $e \cdot e$ can be replaced by e^2 because e is normal to the surface.)

As in the case of a variation in surface impedance the reflection coefficient ϱ, referred to the transverse plane S_0, is obtained by dividing by the impedance change resulting from the insertion of a perfectly reflecting partition. The result, corresponding to eqn. (7.5), is

$$\varrho \simeq \frac{j\omega\xi \int_0^\infty dz \oint_s (\varepsilon e^2 + \mu h \cdot h)_{u=0} f(s, z) \, ds}{2 \iint_{S_0} e \times h \cdot k \, dS} \tag{7.11}$$

It is apparent that the reflection coefficient depends on the energy which would have been stored, in the form of electric and magnetic fields, in the volume displaced by the dent. Only that part of the stored energy which varies with time is significant; the energy stored in a circularly polarized field is constant and makes no contribution to the reflection.

Although the derivation of this result has been simplified by assuming the deformation to be wholly inwards, this assumption is not essential. It is not in fact difficult to generalize the argument, allowing $f(s, z)$ to take both positive and negative values.

The effect of slight inhomogeneity of the dielectric filling a transmission line or waveguide may be treated much the same way as surface irregularities. For this purpose the volume integral formula, eqn. (5.12), is used.

7.2 Effect of the Ground on the Impedance of an Aerial

Some of the perturbation methods described above were evolved in the course of an investigation (Monteath, 1958) into aerials for broadcasting at medium frequencies (in the region of 1 MHz), where the effect of the finite surface impedance of the ground is extremely important; they have also been applied to aerials operating at frequencies as high as 100 MHz and as low as 15 kHz.

The effect of a plane and perfectly conducting earth may readily be taken into account by the method of images. The radiated field for a given input current is determined as the sum of components radiated from the aerial and from its image in the ground. The effect of perfectly conducting ground on the input impedance may be evaluated in terms of the mutual impedance between the aerial and the image, using the induced-e.m.f. method (see Chapter 3). The field produced by a given current and the input resistance together determine the field produced by a given power.

The problem becomes much more complex when ground of finite, and possibly non-uniform, surface impedance is taken into account. Non-uniformity is inevitable in the case of a grounded aerial, such as is used at medium frequencies, since some kind of earth system must be used to enable connection to the ground. Early attempts to calculate the effect of finite ground conductivity on the input impedance were so complex, even in the absence of an earth system, that serious errors were sometimes overlooked.

Let the input impedance of an aerial be Z when the surface impedance of the ground is zero and Z' when the surface impedance is η. Let the magnetic field tangential to the ground due to unit current at the aerial input be h and h' in the two conditions respectively. Equation (6.22) gives

$$Z' - Z = \iint \eta h \cdot h' \, dS \tag{7.12}$$

in which the integral is taken over all that part of the earth's surface which makes a significant contribution to it. In practice it is found that $Z' - Z$ is little affected by regions more than one wavelength from the aerial, and at shorter ranges h' is little different from h. (This

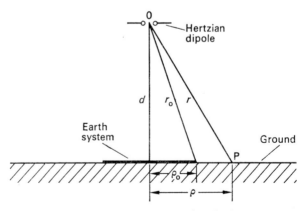

FIG. 7.3. An elevated Hertzian dipole.

statement may be checked by examining the groundwave attenuation factor (Norton, 1936).) Equation (7.12) may therefore be simplified to

$$Z' - Z \simeq \iint \eta h \, . \, h \, dS \tag{7.13}$$

As in similar expressions $h \, . \, h$ may be replaced by h^2 if the tangential component of h is linearly polarized at each point of the surface, a condition satisfied in the particular cases to be considered below.

Figure 7.3 shows a short Hertzian dipole (horizontal in the figure, but vertical dipoles will also be considered) above imperfectly conducting ground. This problem was first considered by Sommerfeld and Renner (1942), who determined the radiation resistance by evaluating the flux of the Poynting vector across infinite parallel planes.† No account was taken of the effect of an earth system, though the desirability of reducing ground losses in this way was pointed out. Equation (7.13) enables the Sommerfeld and Renner results to be derived much more simply, at the same time extending them to determine the reactance as well as the resistance, and to take account of an earth system.

In Fig. 7.3, 0 is the dipole, situated at a height d above the centre of an earth system, which is assumed to reduce the surface impedance to zero over a circle of radius ϱ_0. Let the distance between 0 and a point P on the ground be r, which equals r_0 when P is at the edge of the earth system. In the case of a vertical dipole, the magnetic field is circumferential, its complex magnitude h for unit input current being given by

$$h = (j\beta_0 l/2\pi r^2)(r^2 - d^2)^{1/2}(1 + 1/j\beta_0 r)\exp(-j\beta_0 r) \tag{7.14}$$

where l is the length of the dipole, which is assumed to be short compared with $1/\beta_0$ and with r_0. The change $Z' - Z$ in impedance, due to a change from zero to η in the surface impedance of the ground outside the earth system, is obtained by substituting for h in eqn. (7.13), changing to polar coordinates, and integrating from ϱ_0 to ∞. The

† A more complete treatment has been published by Wait (1969).

result is

$$Z' - Z \simeq \frac{\beta_0^2 l^2 \eta}{2\pi} \left[\frac{j}{\beta_0 r_0} \left(1 - \frac{j}{2\beta_0 r_0} \right) \left(1 - \frac{d^2}{2r_0^2} \right) e^{-2j\beta_0 r_0} \right.$$

$$\left. - \operatorname{Ei}\left(-2j\beta_0 r_0 \right) \right] \qquad (7.15)$$

where

$$\operatorname{Ei}(-jx) = \int_\infty^x \frac{1}{t} e^{-jt} \, dt = \operatorname{Ci}(x) + j \left[\frac{\pi}{2} - \operatorname{Si}(x) \right] \qquad (7.16)$$

For a horizontal dipole h is perpendicular to the dipole, and its complex magnitude, which is independent of azimuth, is given by

$$h = (j\beta_0 I d / 2\pi r^2)(1 + 1/j\beta_0 r) \exp(-j\beta_0 r) \qquad (7.17)$$

$Z' - Z$ is obtained as before; the result is

$$Z' - Z \simeq \frac{j\beta_0 l^2 \eta d}{4\pi r_0^3} \left(1 - \frac{j}{2\beta_0 r_0} \right) e^{-2j\beta_0 r_0} \qquad (7.18)$$

The value of $Z' - Z$ in the absence of an earth system may be obtained by putting r_0 equal to d in eqns. (7.15) and (7.18); and, if the real part is then extracted, it will be found to agree with Sommerfeld and Renner's results.

Equations (7.15) and (7.18) give both resistive and reactive components of $Z' - Z$. Although the reactance of an infinitesimal Hertzian dipole is infinite, a change in reactance has a physical meaning, since the large negative reactance of a short dipole could be tuned out and a change measured directly.

It will be noticed that eqns. (7.15) and (7.18), in common with the results of Sommerfeld and Renner, suggest that in the absence of an earth system the resistance becomes infinite as the height is reduced to zero, even if the ground is a non-conducting dielectric. This absurd result must be due to the failure of the approximations at very low dipole heights. It will be remembered that the concept of surface impedance is applicable only when the tangential magnetic field does not vary greatly between points on the surface less than $1/|\beta|$ apart, where $j\beta$ is the intrinsic propagation constant of the ground. Errors are therefore to be expected when the height of the dipole is comparable to $1/|\beta|$.

Elevated Hertzian dipoles have been considered because of their simplicity and because they had previously been treated by a com-

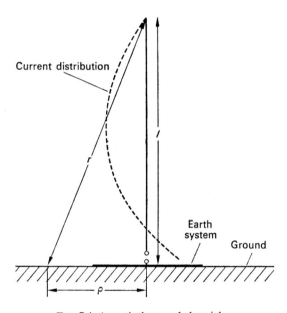

Current distribution

Earth system

Ground

ρ

FIG. 7.4. A vertical grounded aerial.

pletely different method. They provide a useful guide to the behaviour of high-frequency dipoles of finite length.

The simplest aerial used for transmission at medium frequencies, which is shown in Fig. 7.4, is a vertical conductor, such as an insulated mast-radiator, with one end at ground level. It is energized between its lower end and the ground. In high-power installations it is often desirable to suppress radiation towards the ionosphere at certain angles, and this is done by making the effective height a little more than one half-wavelength as shown in the figure. The vertical radiation pattern then has a minimum at some chosen angle, such as 30° or 40°, to the vertical. Such an aerial is termed an "anti-fading aerial".

In order to reduce the physical height required it is common practice to add capacity at the top of a medium-frequency or low-frequency aerial, or to insert a series inductance at an elevated point. It is not difficult to extend the theoretical treatment to take account of these and other complications, but for the sake of simplicity they will be ignored here. Moreover, the current distribution will be assumed to be a sinusoidal standing-wave pattern; in other words the effect of the finite thickness of the aerial will be neglected.

As will appear, the finite surface impedance of the ground is particularly important near the base of a grounded aerial, and steps are usually taken to reduce it in this region by means of a wire mesh or a system of radial wires. The mid-point of this system forms one input terminal. Figure 7.4 shows the ground under the aerial to be covered by such an earth system, which will be assumed to have circular symmetry. The surface impedance η will therefore be treated initially as an arbitrary function of ϱ.

The magnetic field h is everywhere horizontal and tangential to circles centred on the axis of the aerial. Its value at the surface for unit current into the base of the aerial is (Brown, G.H., 1935)

$$h = \frac{j}{2\pi\varrho \sin\beta_0 l} [e^{-j\beta_0 r} - \cos\beta_0 l\, e^{-j\beta_0 l}] \qquad (7.19)$$

The change in self-impedance due to the finite surface impedance is obtained by substituting h, from eqn. (7.19) in eqn. (7.13).

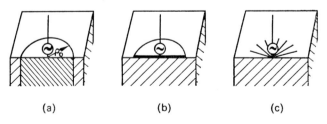

(a)   (b)   (c)

FIG. 7.5. Types of earth system

Figure 7.5(a) (Monteath, 1958) shows an idealized earth system: a circular cylinder (radius ϱ_0) of perfectly conducting metal embedded in the ground. In this case the integrals may be evaluated in closed

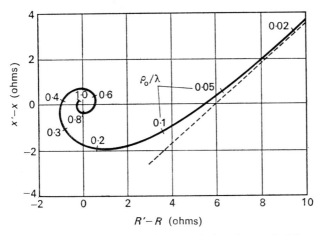

FIG. 7.6. Effect of finite surface impedance on the impedance of a $\lambda/4$ grounded aerial. $\varepsilon_r = 20 - \mathrm{j}180$. Earth system of Fig. 7.5a.

form by taking η to be zero for $\varrho < \varrho_0$ and constant for $\varrho > \varrho_0$. The result is

$$Z' - Z \simeq \frac{\eta}{4\pi} \left[e^{-2\mathrm{j}\beta_0 l} \, \mathrm{Ei} \left\{ -2\mathrm{j}\beta_0 \left(r_0 - l \right) \right\} + e^{2\mathrm{j}\beta_0 l} \, \mathrm{Ei} \left\{ -2\mathrm{j}\beta_0 \left(r_0 + l \right) \right\} \right.$$

$$- 4 \cos \beta_0 l \, e^{-\mathrm{j}\beta_0 l} \, \mathrm{Ei} \left\{ -\mathrm{j}\beta_0 \left(r_0 - l + \varrho_0 \right) \right\}$$

$$- 4 \cos \beta_0 l \, e^{\mathrm{j}\beta_0 l} \, \mathrm{Ei} \left\{ -\mathrm{j}\beta_0 \left(r_0 + l + \varrho_0 \right) \right\}$$

$$+ 4 \cos \beta_0 l \, . \, \mathrm{Ei} \left\{ -\mathrm{j}\beta_0 \left(r_0 + \varrho_0 \right) \right\}$$

$$\left. + 2 \cos^2 \beta_0 l \, . \, \mathrm{Ei} \left(-2\mathrm{j}\beta_0 \varrho_0 \right) \right] \mathrm{cosec}^2 \beta_0 l \qquad (7.20)$$

It is usually preferable (essential if $\beta_0 l \simeq \pi$) to refer the impedance to the current antinode rather than to the input terminals at the base of the aerial. To do this the factor $\mathrm{cosec}^2 \beta_0 l$ should be dropped.

Wait and Surtees (1954) published a more general result taking account of loading with top capacitance.

In Fig. 7.6 (Monteath, 1958) $Z' - Z$ is plotted on the Argand diagram as a function of the radius of the earth system in wavelengths, taking as an example a quarter-wave aerial over highly conducting ground having a relative permittivity of $20 - \text{j}180$. (The imaginary part corresponds to a conductivity of 10^{-2} siemens per metre at 1 MHz.)

Owing to the complexity of eqn. (7.20), its physical significance cannot be appreciated on inspection, and it is instructive to consider limiting cases. For large radii it may be shown that $Z' - Z$ is inversely proportional to the radius of the earth system, suffering a phase retardation which increases by 2π for an increase of one half-wavelength in the radius. The nature of this result suggests that $Z' - Z$ may be regarded as a measure of the reaction upon the aerial of waves reflected from the boundary of the earth system.

For small radii corresponding to the part of the curve which is approaching the asymptote, it may be shown that $Z' - Z$ varies logarithmically with the radius, so that the curve exhibits a tail extending to infinity. In this region each annulus of the ground behaves like an impedance connected in series with the base of the aerial.

The perfectly conducting disc earth system shown in Fig. 7.5(b) will behave in the same way as the cylinder shown in Fig. 7.5(a) apart from a correction for the effect of the sharp edge. Equation (6.19) shows that this correction will be approximately the same in magnitude (but not in phase) as that resulting from a reduction of $1/2|\beta|$ in the radius of the earth system, where $\text{j}\beta$ is the intrinsic propagation constant of the ground. For the case illustrated in Fig. 7.6, $1/2|\beta| = 0 \cdot 006$ wavelengths. The edge effect is negligible so long as ϱ_0 is large in comparison with this.

Figure 7.5(c) shows a radial-wire earth system, the type most commonly used in practice. The usual approach to this problem is to assign to the set of wires a varying surface impedance which, at any point, is assumed to be the same as that of an infinite parallel grating whose wires have the same spacing as that between the radial wires. The surface impedance of this grating is then determined from eqn. (6.20) and combined in parallel with that of the ground. The conditions for the validity of this procedure have been discussed elsewhere (Monteath, 1958). These conditions are not satisfied in the case of a very-low-frequency aerial (for example, one operating at 15 kHz), a problem considered by Wait (1958b).

When the surface impedance varies continuously with the radius, the integration in eqn. (7.13) must be performed numerically.

As might be expected, the outer regions of an earth system tend to have less effect in the case of radial wires than in the case of one of the idealized systems shown in Figs. 7.5(a) and (b). Thus if Fig. 7.6 were re-drawn for a system of (say) 100 radial wires it would be found that the "tail" of the curve ($\varrho_0/\lambda < 0.1$) would be little changed, but the spiral part would tend to be contracted. Graphical results for various practical cases have been published by Wait and Pope (1954, 1955) and by Monteath (1958).

7.3 *Effect of an Earth System on Radiation from an Aerial*

Having considered the effect of finite surface impedance on the input impedance of an aerial, it remains to discuss its effect on the distant field for a given input current, a problem which was not solved until the Compensation Theorem approach had been devised. It proves most convenient to depart from the policy adopted in the previous section and to take as the starting point ground whose surface impedance is finite but uniform (or at least uniform in the vicinity of the aerial). The reasons for this merit discussion.

When we are concerned with radiation at finite angles of elevation the effect of a uniform surface impedance may readily be taken into account by supposing current in the image to be scaled in proportion to the Fresnel reflection coefficient. Any non-uniformity near to the aerial, such as that associated with an earth system, may then be evaluated as a correction. The groundwave, which is important at medium and low frequencies, presents a more complex problem. In addition to the effect of an earth system, or other non-uniformities near to the aerial, it is also necessary to consider the effect of variations in conductivity over the entire path of propagation, which may arise from different geological structures, or from areas of sea which the path has to cross. These effects will be regarded as associated with the path of propagation, rather than with the aerial and earth-system, and will be discussed separately in section 8. The distinction may appear arbitrary but is practically useful for the following reasons. The way in which ground-conductivity affects the impedance of an aerial, and the way in which the earth system affects the radiated field, are dependent on the parameters of the aerial itself—particularly on its height in the case of a simple vertical aerial—whereas these effects can be evaluated without regard to the more distant parts of the path of propagation. On the other hand, the effect of surface impedance over most of the propagation path can be evaluated without regard to the parameters of the transmitting aerial or its earth system.

The groundwave field for a given input current will therefore be evaluated as the product of two factors:

(i) The field that would exist if the earth system were made vanishingly small, while maintaining the current constant. (It is assumed that the earth system is the only cause of non-uniform surface impedance within a wavelength or so of the aerial.) This is considered in Chapter 8.

(ii) The factor by which distant fields are modified by the presence of the earth system, which is discussed in this section.

In Fig. 7.7 (Monteath, 1958), A and B represent respectively the terminals of the transmitting aerial under consideration and those of a distant receiving aerial at ground level. The problem is to determine the ratio in which mutual impedance between A and B is changed when the transmitting aerial is provided with an earth system. For this purpose eqn. (6.22) is used, and Z_{AB} and Z'_{AB} are respectively taken to be the mutual impedance in the absence of an earth system, when the surface impedance in the neighbourhood of A is η, and that in the presence of one, when the surface impedance is η'. The integration may be restricted to the area S occupied by the earth system.

The reduction of eqn. (6.22) to a form suitable for computation will be outlined briefly. Consider the reciprocal form of this equation in which A and B are interchanged. If B is sufficiently distant from A, at all points within S, h_B will be very nearly perpendicular to AB and constant in magnitude, its phase variation from point to point corresponding almost exactly to propagation with the velocity of light. h_A' will be replaced by h_{A0}, the value of h_A for perfectly conducting ground. This is known to be a good approximation because even in the absence of an earth system finite ground conductivity has not

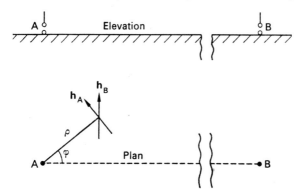

FIG. 7.7. Effect of an earth system on the groundwave field.

much effect on the magnetic field within a wavelength or so of the aerial. Taking polar coordinates (ϱ, ϕ) as shown and writing $h_B(A)$ for the value of h_B at A, we have

$$h_{A0} \cdot h_B = h_{A0} h_B(A)\, e^{j\beta_0 \varrho \cos \phi} \cos \phi \qquad (7.21)$$

It is convenient to express $h_B(A)$ in terms of the mutual impedance Z_{AB} between A and B in the absence of the earth system. In doing so, small corrections for wave tilt and height gain will be neglected, since any error resulting will be a second-order small quantity. Equation (6.22) becomes

$$Z_{AB}' - Z_{AB} = -\frac{Z_{AB}}{l_e \eta_0} \int_0^{\varrho_0} d\varrho \int_0^{2\pi} (\eta' - \eta)\, h_{A0}(\varrho)\, e^{j\beta_0 \varrho \cos \phi} \varrho\, d\phi$$

$$(7.22)$$

where l_e is the effective length of the aerial (i.e. the line integral of the current for unit input current) and ϱ_0 is the radius of the earth system.

Since the mutual impedance is proportional to the groundwave field at B due to unit current in A,

$$Z'_{AB}/Z_{AB} = K \qquad (7.23)$$

where K is the complex ratio in which the groundwave field is changed by the installation of an earth system, the current in the aerial being held constant.

If the earth system has circular symmetry, the integration with respect to ϕ can be performed, when eqn. (7.22) becomes

$$K - 1 = -\frac{2\pi j}{l_e \eta_0} \int_0^{\varrho_0} (\eta' - \eta) \, h_{A0}(\varrho) \, J_1 \, (\beta_0 \varrho) \, \varrho \, d\varrho \qquad (7.24)$$

The integration with respect to ϱ must be performed numerically.

The first-order Bessel function provides a clue to the physical significance of eqn. (7.24), since it occurs also in the expression for the field of a circular loop carrying a uniform current. Suppose the surface to be replaced by an impedance sheet (see Chapter 6) of impedance η across any square. Considering an elementary annulus of the sheet having radii ϱ and $\varrho + d\varrho$, the effect of reducing the surface impedance from η to η' is to reduce the series impedance presented to the surface current crossing it (equal to $2\pi \varrho h_A$) by $(\eta - \eta') \, d\varrho/2\pi\varrho$. The Compensation Theorem for networks suggests that a similar result would be achieved by cutting a narrow annular slot and connecting generators of e.m.f. $h_A \, (\eta' - \eta) \, d\varrho$ across it so as to assist the flow of surface current. Booker's (1946) generalization of Babinet's Principle shows that the radiation field resulting from the excitation of this slot may be calculated by treating it as a magnetic conductor carrying a magnetic current. In this way the right-hand side of eqn. (7.24) may be thought of as the summation of the fields of a large number of elementary annular slots simulating the effect of the earth system.

In Fig. 7.8 (Monteath, 1958), K is plotted on the Argand diagram as a function of ϱ_0, the radius of a perfectly conducting earth system, for a short aerial, height 0.1λ, and an antifading aerial with a height of 0.55λ, over poorly conducting ground. The most striking result is the fact that the groundwave field strength does not change steadily as the radius of the earth system is increased; in fact K traces out a locus resembling a cycloid, becoming stationary at each cusp. The radius corresponding to each cusp is equal to the radius of a loop aerial that would not radiate in its own plane. The cycloidal form of the curves suggests that the change in groundwave field caused by the

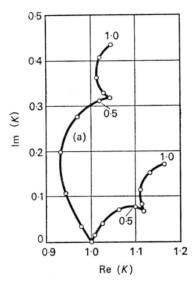

FIG. 7.8. Variation of groundwave field with radius of earth system (of Fig. 7.5a). (a) 0.1λ aerial. (b) 0.55λ aerial. $\varepsilon_r = 5 - j18$. The parameter is ϱ_0/λ. Points are plotted at 0.1λ intervals but in (b) the points for $\varrho_0 = 0$ and $\varrho_0 = 0.1\lambda$ are indistinguishable.

earth system may be regarded as the sum of two components, one increasing steadily as the radius of the system increases, the other decreasing slowly in magnitude while its phase becomes progressively more retarded. The first component is associated with the elimination of groundwave attenuation along that part of the path of propagation passing over the earth system; the second is the result of reflection from the discontinuity occurring at the boundary of the system behind the aerial. This explanation has been confirmed by considering a semi-circular earth system oriented to produce either component separately.

Results for various cases, including sectoral earth systems, have been published by Monteath (1958) and by Wait (1956a, 1963a, 1967).

Up to this point we have considered only the groundwave field, but the analysis may readily be extended to determine the effect of an earth system on the vertical radiation pattern. Referring to Fig. 7.7, the reference aerial B is supposed to be elevated to each angle of elevation in turn. The principal modification of eqn. (7.24) is the replacement of $J_1 (\beta_0 \varrho)$ by $J_1 (\beta_0 \varrho \sin \theta)$, where θ is the angle to the vertical. (Note that $J_1 (\beta_0 \varrho \sin \theta)$ corresponds to the vertical radiation pattern of a horizontal loop of radius ϱ.) Some results for various practical cases have been derived and experimentally confirmed using models (Monteath, 1958).

Wait and Spies (1970) have determined the radiation pattern of a short-wave aerial over a radial earth system which is so large (in wavelengths) that it is not permissible to neglect the effect of finite surface impedance on the tangential magnetic field, since groundwave attenuation may be significant. Instead of replacing h'_A by h_{A0} as in eqn. (7.21), h'_A was determined by using the compensation theorem to set up an integral equation.

Chapter 8

PERTURBATION METHODS APPLIED TO GROUNDWAVE PROPAGATION

8.1 *Introductory*

Groundwave propagation over imperfectly conducting earth has received much attention over many years; the reader is referred to articles by Wait (1964a, 1962) for a review of published work and for self-contained derivations of the principal results. Even for a homogeneous plane earth Sommerfeld's original solution was not simple; Baños (1966) has devoted an authoritative monograph to an exhaustive study of it. Sommerfeld's method was equivalent to resolving spherical waves diverging from the source into an angular spectrum of plane waves and supposing each elementary plane wave to be reflected by the ground in accordance with the appropriate Fresnel reflection coefficient. A simple approach based on Huygens' Principle has been outlined in Chapter 4, but this leads only to the limiting result at long range, where the value of a plane-earth solution is very restricted.

In order to take the spherical form of the earth into account, the continuous angular spectrum of plane waves is replaced by a series of zonal harmonics, which is slowly convergent, but has been transformed into a more useful series by Watson. A thorough exposition of the theory has been given by Bremmer (1949).

The results of the classical theories referred to above were reduced to a convenient form for engineering use by K. A. Norton (1936, 1937, 1941).

The effect of inhomogeneous ground has been studied by many workers from 1944 onwards, using three principal methods. The first of these, due to Feinberg, is a perturbation method based on Green's theorem, which will be discussed in Chapter 9. Secondly, Clemmow (1966) used dual integral equations to study propagation across a straight boundary between regions of a plane earth having different ground constants. This elegant method cannot readily be extended to more complex cases. The third approach, which is followed in the remainder of this chapter, is a perturbation method based on eqns. (5.30) and (6.22), which leads to substantially the same mathematical formulation as does the Green's theorem method, but seems more easily understood. It permits both non-uniform surface impedance and non-uniform curvature to be taken into account, but it also provides the simplest treatment of a uniform plane or spherical earth.

Section 8.2 deals with reflection at a boundary between two regions of differing surface impedance, such as a coastline. Section 8.3 considers propagation over a plane earth of non-uniform surface impedance, obtaining the attenuation factor for a homogeneous plane earth as a byproduct, and section 8.4 extends this treatment to include non-uniform curvature. Finally the scattering of the groundwave by irregularities is discussed in section 8.5.

8.2 *Reflection at a Boundary*

In this section we shall consider a plane earth comprising two regions of different surface impedance separated by a straight boundary.

In Fig. 8.1 (Monteath, 1951) the y-axis is the boundary, the surface impedance being η' for $x > 0$ and zero for $x < 0$. A and B represent two short vertical grounded aerials at ground level; their distances from the boundary will be assumed to be at least several wavelengths. Suppose that the surface impedance is initially zero everywhere, and that it then changes to η' for $x > 0$. The effect of reflection at the boundary may be expressed in terms of the resulting change from Z_{AB} to Z'_{AB} in the mutual impedance.

Putting $\eta = 0$, eqn. (6.22) gives:

$$Z'_{AB} - Z_{AB} = \eta' \int_0^\infty dx \int_{-\infty}^\infty \mathbf{h}_A \cdot \mathbf{h}'_B \, dy \qquad (8.1)$$

where, as before, primed symbols denote quantities existing after the change in surface impedance. The suffix t has been dropped from h_A and h'_B because the magnetic field is everywhere parallel to the surface.

Application of the principle of stationary phase to the integral leads to the conclusion that the predominant contribution comes from elements of the surface close to Q, the point on the boundary at which optical reflection would occur. It is therefore permissible to replace

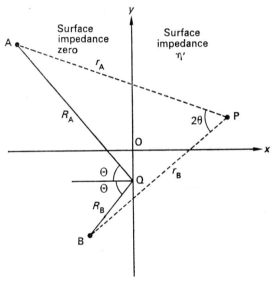

FIG. 8.1. Reflection at a land–sea boundary.

h'_B by h_B, on the assumption that h'_B is not greatly affected by the change in surface impedance at points within one half-wavelength of the boundary. The equation then becomes

$$Z'_{AB} - Z_{AB} \simeq \eta' \int_0^\infty dx \int_{-\infty}^\infty h_A h_B \cos 2\theta \, dy \qquad (8.2)$$

where θ is defined in Fig. 8.1.

It may be helpful to amplify the justification given above for ignoring the effect of errors in h'_B at points remote from Q. Suppose that the integration is first performed with respect to y and that we then proceed to integrate with respect to x, summing contributions made by elementary strips parallel to the boundary. These contributions will be progressively retarded in phase as x increases, but their amplitudes will diminish only slowly, so that if the integral were plotted on the Argand diagram its locus would trace out a spiral. Any error in the integrand which is small for $x < \lambda/2$ and which changes only slowly thereafter may change the tightness of the spiral, but will not greatly affect the position of the asymptotic point towards which it converges.

The final stages of the analysis will be summarized briefly. h_A and h_B are obtained from eqn. (7.14), by putting d equal to zero and ignoring $1/\beta_0 r_A$ and $1/\beta_0 r_B$ compared with unity. The quantities r_A, r_B and θ may be replaced by R_A, R_B and Θ, their values at Q, except in the exponents. By again using the fact that $1/\beta_0 r_A$ and $1/\beta_0 r_B$ are small, the integration may be carried out; the result is

$$Z'_{AB} - Z_{AB} \simeq \frac{\beta_0^2 l^2 \eta'}{4\pi} \cdot \frac{\cos 2\Theta}{\cos^2 \Theta} \cdot \frac{\exp\left[-j\beta_0 (R_A + R_B) + j\pi/4\right]}{\sqrt{\left[2\pi\beta_0^3 R_A R_B (R_A + R_B)\right]}}$$

(8.3)

Now if A and B had been placed at a distance $(R_A + R_B)$ from one another over a uniform and perfectly conducting earth, their mutual impedance would have been

$$\frac{j\beta_0 \eta_0 l^2 \exp\left[-j\beta_0 (R_A + R_B)\right]}{2\pi (R_A + R_B)}$$

(8.4)

If this expression is divided into the right-hand side of eqn. (8.3), the quotient may be described as the *apparent reflection coefficient* at the boundary. It is given by

$$\varrho \simeq \frac{\exp(-j\pi/4)}{4\pi} \cdot \frac{\eta'}{\eta_0} \cdot \sqrt{\frac{\lambda (R_A + R_B)}{R_A R_B}} \cdot \frac{\cos 2\Theta}{\cos^2 \Theta}$$

(8.5)

This expression contains R_A and R_B and it is not, therefore, a true reflection coefficient; for example, ϱ is proportional to $R_B^{-1/2}$ if $R_A \gg R_B$. A physical explanation is that, although optical reflection occurs in the horizontal plane, the reflected rays diverge from the boundary in the vertical plane; in this respect the boundary behaves like a polished metal wire reflecting light. It is noteworthy that, to the order of accuracy attained, ϱ is zero when the angle of incidence is $\pi/4$, but becomes large near grazing incidence.

The analysis may be extended to cases in which the surface impedance is not zero on the nearer side of the boundary. If it is η_1 and η_2 on the nearer and further sides respectively, η' should be replaced in eqn. (8.5) by $\eta_2 - \eta_1$. The incident and reflected waves will then be subject to the normal ground-wave attenuation appropriate to the path lengths R_A and R_B respectively.

Results in more complex cases have been derived by Wait (1963b). Experimental confirmation has been obtained by King and Maley (1965, 1966).

If the boundary is not straight, the reflection will be governed by two-dimensional optical considerations, so that a concave boundary may exhibit a focusing effect.

8.3 *Propagation over a Plane Inhomogeneous Earth*

Figure 8.2 illustrates the simplest problem, in which two regions of surface impedance η_1 and η_2 are separated by a boundary, the y-axis. Two short grounded aerials A and B are situated on either side of the boundary, at least a few wavelengths from it. It is assumed that the boundary is straight and perpendicular to AB, although this condition is not important. The following treatment, due to Wait (1956b), differs from applications of perturbation methods discussed so far in as much as the change to be evaluated need not be small.

Consider three cases:

I. The surface impedance is η_1 everywhere. The magnetic field due to unit current in aerial A(B) is $h_A(h_B)$ and the mutual impedance is Z_{AB}.

II. As shown in Fig. 8.2, the surface impedance is η_1 for $x < 0$ and η_2 for $x > 0$. The magnetic field due to unit current in A(B) is $h'_A(h'_B)$ and the mutual impedance is Z'_{AB}.

III. The surface impedance is η_2 everywhere. The magnetic field due to unit current in aerial A(B) is $h''_A(h''_B)$.

Equation (6.22) is used to determine the effect of a change from Case I to Case II, giving

$$Z'_{AB} - Z_{AB} = (\eta_2 - \eta_1) \int_0^\infty dx \int_{-\infty}^\infty h''_A \cdot h'_B \, dy \qquad (8.6)$$

The integration is carried out only on the right of the boundary where the surface impedance has changed. h_A will be regarded as known

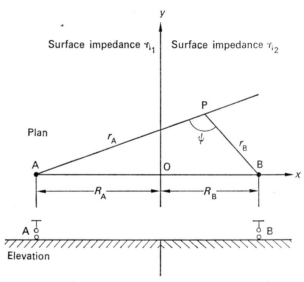

FIG. 8.2. Propagation over a two-part plane earth.

since it is the result of propagation over a homogeneous earth of surface impedance η_1. Let the complex attenuation factor for this case (that is the complex ratio in which the fields are reduced because of the finite surface impedance) at a range r be $G(r, \eta_1)$, so that

$$h_A = h_{A0} G(r_A, \eta_1) \qquad (8.7)$$

where h_{A0} is the field that would exist at the point P if the surface impedance were zero.

Now the value of h'_B for a point on the right of the boundary would be the result of propagation over homogeneous ground of surface impedance η_2 (Case III) but for the effect of reflection at the boundary. This is a second-order effect and the analysis of section 8.2 shows that the error caused by neglecting it is very small indeed. We may therefore write

$$h'_B \simeq h''_B = h_{B0} G(r_B, \eta_2) \tag{8.8}$$

It is also convenient to write

$$Z'_{AB} = Z_{AB0} G(R_A, \eta_1; R_B, \eta_2) \tag{8.9}$$

where Z_{AB0} is the mutual impedance that would exist if the surface mpedance were everywhere zero. Equation (8.6) becomes

$$[G(R_A, \eta_1; R_B, \eta_2) - G(R_A + R_B, \eta_1)] Z_{AB0}$$

$$\simeq (\eta_2 - \eta_1) \int_0^\infty dx \int_{-\infty}^\infty h_{A0} h_{B0} \cos \psi G(r_A, \eta_1) G(r_B, \eta_2) \, dy \tag{8.10}$$

Now h_{A0}, h_{B0} and Z_{AB} are known (eqns. (7.14) with $d = 0$ and eqn. (8.4)):

$$h_{A0} = \frac{j\beta_0 l}{2\pi r_A} (1 + 1/j\beta_0 r_A) e^{-j\beta_0 r_A} \tag{8.11}$$

and similarly for h_{B0}.

$$Z_{AB0} \simeq \frac{j\beta_0 \eta_0 l^2}{2\pi (R_A + R_B)} e^{-j\beta_0 (R_A + R_B)} \tag{8.12}$$

neglecting the induction field at a range $R_A + R_B$. Substituting in eqn. (8.10) gives

$$G(R_A, \eta_1; R_B, \eta_2) \simeq G(R_A + R_B, \eta_1)$$

$$+ \frac{j\beta_0 (\eta_2 - \eta_1)}{2\pi\eta_0} \int_0^\infty dx \int_{-\infty}^\infty \left[1 + \frac{1}{j\beta_0 r_A}\right]\left[1 + \frac{1}{j\beta_0 r_B}\right] G(r_A, \eta_1) \times$$

$$\times G(r_B, \eta_2) \cos \psi \frac{R_A + R_B}{r_A r_B} e^{-j\beta_0 (r_A + r_B - R_A - R_B)} \, dy \tag{8.13}$$

At this point a number of approximations are made. These are all based on the assumption that no significant contributions to the integral are made by regions within one or two wavelengths of A or B. It is clear that the vicinity of A need not be considered because A is assumed to be at least a few wavelengths to the left of the boundary, but the justification for ignoring the vicinity of B is less obvious. Detailed consideration of this matter will be deferred, but it is reasonable to expect that any error will be at least fairly small since consideration of earth systems (by the method described in section 7.3) has shown that the surface impedance within a wavelength or two of either aerial will not change the received signal by more than about 20%.

Bearing in mind that $\beta_0 r_A$ is assumed to be large in regions making an important contribution to the integral, and that $\cos \psi$ is a factor of the integrand, it follows that $\beta_0 |R_B - x|$ may be assumed to be large. The principle of stationary phase then leads to the conclusion that the major contribution to the integral will be made in the vicinity of the straight line AB, since the phase of the integrand is retarded rapidly on moving away from this line. If also the region to the right of B is ignored (this assumption will be reviewed later) the integrand may be simplified by putting

$$
\left.
\begin{aligned}
r_A &\simeq R_A + x \\
r_B &\simeq R_B - x \\
\cos \psi &\simeq -1
\end{aligned}
\right\}
\tag{8.14}
$$

except in the exponent. The exponent may be expanded in powers of y and terms in y^4, y^6, etc., discarded. This process gives

$$
r_A + r_B - R_A - R_B \simeq \frac{y^2 (R_A + R_B)}{2 (R_A + x) (R_B - x)}
\tag{8.15}
$$

Making these approximations, neglecting $1/\beta_0 r_A$ and $1/\beta_0 r_B$ in comparison with unity, and performing the integration with respect to y, eqn. (8.13) becomes

$$G (R_A, \eta_1; R_B, \eta_2)$$

$$\simeq G (R_A + R_B, \eta_1) - \sqrt{\frac{j\beta_0}{2\pi}} \cdot \frac{\eta_2 - \eta_1}{\eta_0} \times$$

$$\times \int_0^{R_0} G (R_A + x, \eta_1) \, G (R_B - x, \eta_2) \sqrt{\frac{R_A + R_B}{(R_A + x) (R_B - x)}} \, dx$$

$$(8.16)$$

The attenuation factor for a homogeneous earth cannot generally be expressed more simply than in terms of an error function or Fresnel integral of a complex variable. It is therefore generally necessary to evaluate the integral in eqn. (8.16) numerically, but solutions in closed form have been obtained in limiting cases (Wait, 1956b). For example, if R_A and R_B are sufficiently large, the result confirms eqn. (4.20).

The derivation of eqn. (8.16) was based on certain approximations which were not fully justified in Wait's original paper. Referring to Fig. 8.3(a), the integration ought to have been extended over the right-hand half-plane, but in fact it was restricted to the shaded area. Even within this area there were a number of approximations which would not be valid within a wavelength or so of B. These difficulties may be overcome by integrating separately over the areas marked S_1 and S_2 in Fig. 8.3(b), where the radius R of the circle is of the order of one wavelength. It is not difficult to justify the exclusion of the unshaded region between S_1 and S_2. Within S_1 the approximations are readily justified. For a point P within S_2 it is permissible to replace $G (r_A, \eta_1)$ and $G (r_B, \eta_2)$ by $G (R_A + R_B, \eta_1^{-})$ and unity respectively, and to regard AP as parallel to the x-axis. If these simplifications are made the approximations made previously may be avoided within S_2, but the integral must be evaluated numerically. This integral is the same as that in eqn. (7.24), which was concerned with the effect of circular earth systems. The result obtained in this way is found to agree with eqn. (8.16) to about 1%. This agreement seems to some extent fortuitous, since it becomes worse if the right-hand half of the circular area S_2 is neglected. In other words the error due to neglecting the region

$x > R_B$ was compensated for by the effect of the other approximations. This justification of Wait's approximations may also be applied to more complex cases which will be discussed later.

These results have been extended to include the case when one of the two aerials is near the boundary (Wait, 1957b; Millar, 1967), to oblique propagation across a boundary (Wait, 1963b; Wait and Jackson, 1963) and to radiation obliquely upwards (Andersen, 1963). The last case relates to propagation via the ionosphere. Christiansen

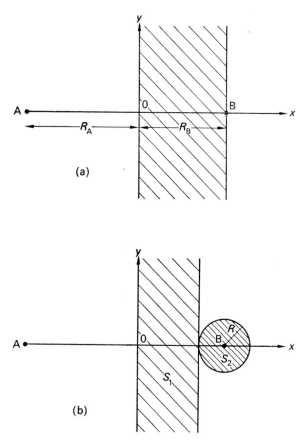

Fig. 8.3. Area of integration. (a) Wait's treatment. (b) Alternative considered.

and Larsen (1967) have considered ground whose surface comprises irregular areas of differing conductivity. A blurred boundary, across which the surface impedance changes linearly, has also been considered (Wait, 1964b; Wait and Spies, 1964). Andersen (1967) has applied the same technique to a surface wave launcher consisting of a small feed aerial above a semi-infinite reactive surface.

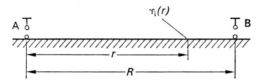

FIG. 8.4. Continuously varying surface impedance.

Equation (8.16) may readily be extended to take account of a surface impedance varying continuously along the path of propagation. Again we consider a change from Case I to Case II where these are as follows:

    I. The surface impedance is zero everywhere. The groundwave attenuation factor is unity.

    II. The surface impedance is $\eta(r)$, an arbitrary function of the distance r from the transmitter along the path of propagation (Fig. 8.4). The groundwave attenuation factor at a range R is $G(R, \eta)$, which will depend on η in the range $0 < r < R$, but will be regarded as independent of η for $r > R$.

Equation (8.16) is found to be replaced by

$$G(R) \simeq 1 - \sqrt{\frac{j\beta_0}{2\pi}} \int_0^R \frac{\eta(r)}{\eta_0} G(r) \sqrt{\frac{R}{r(R-r)}} \cdot dr \qquad (8.17)$$

Experimental confirmation of these results, applied to paths consisting of two or three sections with different surface impedances, has been obtained by Maley and Ottesen (1964) and by King, Maley and Wait (1966).

Although the compensation theorem was invoked to deal with inhomogeneous ground, it does in fact offer the simplest derivation of Sommerfeld's result for a homogeneous earth. If η is a constant, eqn. (8.17) becomes

$$G(R, \eta) = 1 - \sqrt{\frac{j\beta_0}{2\pi} \frac{\eta}{\eta_0}} \int_0^R G(r, \eta) \sqrt{\frac{R}{r(R-r)}} \, dr \qquad (8.18)$$

The range R will now be expressed in terms of a complex dimensionless "numerical distance" P given by

$$P = -\frac{1}{2} j\beta_0 \left(\frac{\eta}{\eta_0}\right)^2 R \qquad (8.19)$$

Equation (8.18) becomes

$$G(R, \eta) = F(P) \qquad (8.20)$$

where

$$F(P) = 1 - \frac{j}{\sqrt{\pi}} \int_0^P F(u) \sqrt{\frac{P}{u(P-u)}} \, du \qquad (8.21)$$

Hufford (1952), who used the Green's Theorem method (see Chapter 9) as a starting point, has shown that this equation may be solved analytically to give the well-known Sommerfeld formula

$$F(P) = 1 - j \sqrt{\pi P} \, e^{-P} \, \mathrm{erfc} \, (j\sqrt{P}) \qquad (8.22)$$

For small values of P it is very easy to obtain an expansion of $F(P)$ in ascending powers of $P^{1/2}$ by an iterative process. The $(n+1)$th approximation is expressed in terms of the nth approximation $F_n(P)$:

$$F_{n+1}(P) = 1 - \frac{j}{\sqrt{\pi}} \int_0^P F_n(u) \sqrt{\frac{P}{u(P-u)}} \, du \qquad (8.23)$$

Putting $F_0(P) = 1$, iteration leads to the well-known series

$$F(P) \sim 1 - j\sqrt{\pi P} - 2P \ldots \qquad (8.24)$$

King (1969) has used the compensation theorem as above to obtain more general solutions including elevated aerials and both polarizations.

8.4 *Propagation over an Inhomogeneous Earth of Varying Curvature*

The extension of eqn. (8.18) to include ground which is not flat and whose surface impedance and curvature both vary from point to point is surprisingly simple. The following outline is based on Hufford's (1952) treatment, but uses eqn. (5.30) rather than the Green's Theorem approach followed by Hufford.†

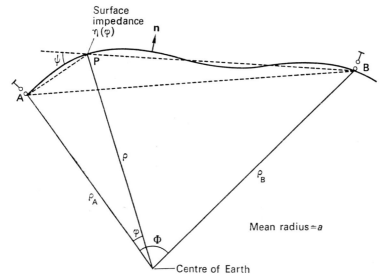

FIG. 8.5. Propagation over inhomogeneous ground of varying curvature.

It will be assumed for simplicity that the range R is short in comparison with the radius of the earth, less than about 1000 km. Relaxation of this condition complicates the expressions but entails no fundamental difficulty (Wait, 1964a). It will also be assumed that the slope of the ground is nowhere too steep. To save space various simplifications arising from these assumptions will be taken for granted.

† The compensation theorem method has been applied to a curved inhomogeneous earth by Wait and Householder (1957), Wait (1958a, 1961 and 1964a) and by Wait and Walters (1963). See Wait (1962) for a useful survey.

Referring to Fig. 8.5, the polar coordinates (ϱ, ϕ), represent a point on the curved propagation path APB. An attenuation factor $G\,(a\Phi)$ represents the ratio in which the coupling between A and B is reduced by the curvature and finite surface impedance,† where a is the mean radius of the earth.

Equation (5.30) is used to determine the effect of a change from the plane perfectly conducting surface AB (unprimed quantities) to the curved surface APB having a surface impedance η which varies smoothly from point to point (primed quantities).

The reciprocal version of eqn. (6.1) is

$$Z'_{AB} = Z_{AB} + \iint_S (e_B \times h'_A - e'_A \times h_B)\,.\,\mathbf{n}\,dS \qquad (8.25)$$

The surface S comprises both the plane and curved surfaces, but the former makes no contribution. The field components tangential to the curved surface at P are given by:

$$h'_A = \frac{j\beta_0 l}{2\pi\,(AP)}\,e^{-j\beta_0(AP)}\,G\,(a\phi) \qquad (8.26)$$

$$h_B = -\frac{j\beta_0 l}{2\pi\,(BP)}\,e^{-j\beta_0(BP)} \qquad (8.27)$$

$$e'_{At} = -\eta h'_A \qquad (8.28)$$

$$e_{Bt} = \eta_0 \psi h_B \qquad (8.29)$$

where l is the effective length of each aerial and ψ is, as shown, the inclination of the straight line BP to the surface at P. A positive magnetic field is directed into the paper while a tangential electric field such as e'_{Bt} is directed from A towards B. $\mathbf{n}$ is directed along the upward normal. Distances such as (AP) are measured in a straight line.

$$Z_{AB} = \frac{j\beta_0 \eta_0 l^2}{2\pi\,(AB)}\,e^{-j\beta_0(AB)} \qquad (8.30)$$

† In the interests of simplicity the reference condition is taken to be propagation over a plane perfectly conducting earth, the path length being equal to the chord AB (Fig. 8.5) rather than the arc APB.

and

$$Z'_{AB} = Z_{AB} G(a\Phi) \tag{8.31}$$

Equation (8.25) becomes

$$G(a\Phi)$$
$$= 1 - \frac{j\beta_0}{2\pi} \iint_S \left(\psi + \frac{\eta}{\eta_0}\right) e^{-j\beta_0[(AP)+(PB)-(AB)]} \frac{(AB)}{(AP)(PB)} G(a\phi)\, dS \tag{8.32}$$

As in the derivation of eqn. (8.16) integration is first performed with respect to a coordinate y directed along the surface perpendicularly to the path of propagation. (Variations of height and surface impedance with y are assumed to be reasonably slow, so that the principle of stationary phase permits them to be ignored.) This gives

$$G(a\Phi) \simeq 1 - \sqrt{\frac{j\beta_0}{2\pi}} \int_0^\phi \left(\psi + \frac{\eta}{\eta_0}\right) \frac{(AB)}{\sqrt{(AP)(PB)[(AP)+(PB)]}} \times$$
$$\times e^{-j\beta_0[(AP)+(PB)-(AB)]} G(a\phi)\, a\, d\phi \tag{8.33}$$

Here an element of length measured along the surface has been approximated by $a\, d\phi$. It is also permissible to replace (AB), (AP) and (PB) by distances measured along the mean sphere except in the exponent.

Writing

$$\xi = \beta_0 [(AP) + (PB) - (AB)]$$
$$R = a\Phi$$
$$r = a\phi$$

Equation (8.33) becomes

$$G(R) = 1 - \sqrt{\frac{j\beta_0}{2\pi}} \int_0^R \left(\psi + \frac{\eta}{\eta_0}\right) e^{-j\xi} \sqrt{\frac{R}{r(R-r)}} G(r)\, dr \tag{8.34}$$

This is the same as eqn. (8.17) with η replaced by the fictitious surface impedance η_c:

$$\eta_c = (\psi\eta_0 + \eta)\, e^{-j\xi} \qquad (8.35)$$

If the earth is perfectly spherical it may be shown that

$$\xi \simeq \frac{\beta_0 Rr\,(R - r)}{8a^2}$$

and

$$\psi \simeq \frac{R - r}{2a}$$

Equation (8.34) becomes

$$G(R) = 1 - \sqrt{\frac{j\beta_0}{2\pi}} \int_0^R \left(\frac{R - r}{a} + \frac{\eta}{\eta_0}\right) \times$$

$$\times\, e^{-j\beta_0 Rr(R-r)/8a^2} \sqrt{\frac{R}{r\,(R - r)}}\; G(r)\, dr \qquad (8.36)$$

If it is preferred to use an attenuation factor $G_1(R)$ for which the reference path is over a plane perfectly conducting earth, but is equal in length to the actual curved path, it is necessary to replace $G(R)$ by $G_1(R)\, e^{-j\beta_0 R^3/24a^2}$ to take into account the difference between the length of the arc APB and the chord AB (and similarly for $G(r)$).

Hufford (1952) has solved an equation equivalent to eqn. (8.36) by expressing the right-hand side as a convolution integral and taking Laplace transforms. This is probably the simplest method of solving the problem of a homogeneous spherical earth.

Equations (8.18) and (8.17), which apply to a homogeneous and an inhomogeneous plane earth respectively, and eqns. (8.36) and (8.34), which apply to a spherical earth and an irregular earth respectively, are all integral equations of the Volterra type. They express the unknown function of an argument R in terms of the values of that function for all arguments smaller than R. Ott and Berry (1970) have shown that it is possible to write a programme for solving these equations numerically and have demonstrated that it correctly solves the problem of a homogeneous spherical earth. Extension of this procedure to the most complex case (eqn. (8.34)) should be possible.

8.5 *Scattering of a Groundwave by an Irregular Surface*

When waves are reflected by an irregular surface some of the energy is scattered away from the direction of specular reflection. Equation (5.30) may be used to determine a first-order approximation to the scattered field provided that the irregularity of the surface, expressed in terms of the gradient, is sufficiently slight. A and B are regarded as the input terminals of two dipoles, one of which is the source of the incident waves while the other is used to detect the scattered waves. This procedure has proved useful in relation to anti-fading aerials used for broadcasting at medium frequencies.

An anti-fading aerial is intended to provide a broadcasting service by means of the groundwave, but at night waves reflected from the ionosphere ("skywaves") cause fading at greater ranges. The aerial is therefore designed to reduce radiation directed obliquely upwards, and its vertical radiation pattern is often arranged to have a minimum at an angle to the vertical which is carefully controlled, usually between 30° and 45°. Unless the ground is very flat over an area extending many wavelengths from the aerial, scattered waves can effectively fill in this minimum and increase fading in the outer parts of the area served, where the groundwave has been weakened by the finite surface impedance.

Consider in the first place the configuration shown in Fig. 8.6 in which the surface of the ground is nowhere below a plane passing through the base of the aerial A. Aerial B is, as usual, a short Hertzian dipole, its distance R from A is assumed to be very great in comparison with any other distance involved. Let the effective lengths of the aerials (i.e. the line integral of the current divided by the input current) be l_A and l_B.

It is possible to take account of a non-uniform surface impedance, which can in principle cause scattering even if the surface is flat, but the variations are usually too gradual to have a significant effect. If the surface impedance is taken to be small and uniform, and if the gradient of the surface is small, it is permissible to regard these as making independent contributions to the scattered field. Since the effect of a finite but uniform surface impedance can be taken into account by elementary methods it is necessary only to consider scattering by a perfectly conducting irregular surface. It is, however, easy to introduce a correction for groundwave attenuation.

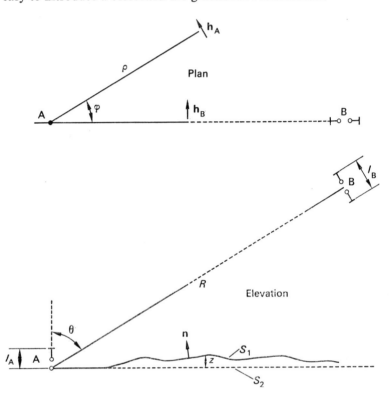

FIG. 8.6. Scattering of the groundwave by an irregular surface.

As in other examples the scattered field is expressed in terms of $Z'_{AB} - Z_{AB}$, where primed and unprimed quantities refer respectively to situations in which the ground is irregular and flat. Use may be made either of eqn. (5.30) or of the reciprocal version with A and B interchanged. In either case the integral need be taken only over the upper surface S_1 because S_2 makes no contribution to the integral.

Moreover, since the ground is assumed to be perfectly conducting neither e'_A nor e'_B has any tangential component. The alternative equations are therefore:

$$Z'_{AB} - Z_{AB} = \iint_{S_1} (e_A \times h'_B) \cdot n \, dS \tag{8.37}$$

and

$$Z'_{AB} - Z_{AB} = \iint_{S_1} (e_B \times h'_A) \cdot n \, dS \tag{8.38}$$

where n is a unit vector in the direction of the upward normal. If eqn. (8.37) is used a valid approximation is to put the tangential component of h'_B equal to twice that of the free-space field at the same point. In the case of eqn. (8.38) the tangential component of h'_A is assumed to be approximately equal to that of h_A for the same value of ϱ. This approximation has the merit of being justified by experience, in that the horizontal magnetic field of a vertical aerial is known to be but little affected by gently undulating ground. In practice eqn. (8.37) proves less simple because it is necessary to take into account both the vertical and horizontal components of e_A, a significant contribution to the latter being made by the induction field. Equation (8.38) is therefore preferable.

Taking into account reflection by the original plane surface, e_B is found to have a component,

$$-\frac{j\beta_0 \eta_0 l_B}{4\pi R} \sin\theta \, e^{-j\beta_0(R - \varrho \cos\phi \sin\theta)} \left(e^{j\beta_0 z \cos\theta} + e^{-j\beta_0 z \cos\theta}\right)$$

directed vertically upwards. This gives a component of $e_B \times h'_A$ which is horizontal and directed along radials from A, and which contributes to the flux of $e_B \times h'_A$ across S_1 only if $\partial z/\partial\varrho$ is not zero. The horizontal component of $e_B^\bullet$ is

$$\frac{j\beta_0 \eta_0 l_B}{4\pi R} \cos\theta \, e^{-j\beta_0(R - \varrho \cos\phi \sin\theta)} \left(e^{j\beta_0 z \cos\theta} - e^{-j\beta_0 z \cos\theta}\right)$$

directed along the ($\phi = 0$) radial. This gives a vertical component of

$e_B \times h'_A$ varying as $\cos \phi$. The direction of positive currents and magnetic fields are as shown.

Let the vertical radiation pattern of aerial A over the plane surface be expressed in terms of a function $F(\theta)$ (which will in general be complex) and let the scattered field add to $F(\theta)$ a component $\Delta F(\theta)$. Use will be made of the fact that the mutual impedance for $\theta = \pi/2$ in the case of a plane surface is

$$\frac{j\beta_0 \eta_0 I_A I_B}{2\pi R} e^{-j\beta_0 R}$$

Equation (8.38) becomes:

$$\frac{\Delta F(\theta)}{F(\pi/2)} \simeq -\frac{1}{I_A} \int_0^\infty d\varrho \int_0^{2\pi} \left[\sin\theta \cos(\beta_0 z \cos\theta) \frac{\partial z}{\partial \varrho} \right.$$
$$\left. - j \cos\theta \sin(\beta_0 z \cos\theta) \cos\phi \right] e^{j\beta_0 \varrho \sin\theta \cos\phi} h_A(\varrho) \varrho \, d\phi$$

(8.39)

The area of an element of S_1 has here been approximated by that of its projection upon S_2: $\varrho \, d\varrho \, d\phi$. Although the gradient of the surface has been assumed small the validity of this result does not depend on $\beta_0 z$ being small.

If it is required to take account of irregularities many wavelengths from the aerial it is advisable to take groundwave attenuation into account by applying the attenuation factor appropriate to the range when computing $h_A(\varrho)$.

Equation (8.39) gives only the vertically polarized component of the scattered radiation, but in practice it is generally required to obtain the horizontal component also, because the polarization of the skywave is changed in the course of reflection by the ionosphere. This may be done by assuming B to be a horizontal dipole. The two components may then be combined to obtain the ordinary-wave and extra-ordinary-wave components; often only the former need be considered, because of stronger absorption of the latter in the ionosphere.

It is possible to derive eqn. (8.39) by an alternative method (Page and Monteath, 1955) which appears physically much simpler, although it does not, in the author's opinion, justify the approximations quite so convincingly. It is supposed that the ground is initially flat and that current is then impressed over a surface corresponding to that of the hill. This impressed current distribution is assumed to be the same as that originally flowing in the plane surface, and its distant field is computed, taking account of reflection by the plane surface below.

The procedures outlined above require modification if parts of the surface are below the base of the aerial. One method is to assume the unperturbed plane surface S_2 to pass through the base of the aerial, and to use eqns. (8.37) and (8.38) to determine the effect of those parts of S_1 which are respectively below and above S_2 respectively. We then have

$$Z'_{AB} - Z_{AB} \simeq \iint_{S_1} (e_B \times h'_A) \cdot \mathbf{n} \, dS + \iint_{S_2} (e'_B \times h_A) \cdot \mathbf{n} \, dS$$

(8.40)

where the first term is applicable where $z > 0$ and the second where $z < 0$. Alternatively, the unperturbed plane surface may be taken at the level of the lowest point of the ground, and therefore below the base of the aerial. In either way it is possible to justify the application of eqn. (8.40) to negative values of z.

In the special case of circular symmetry, integration may be performed with respect to ϕ, whereupon eqn. (8.39) becomes

$$\frac{\Delta F(\theta)}{F(\pi/2)} \simeq -\frac{2\pi}{l_A} \int_0^\infty \left[\sin \theta \cos (\beta_0 z \cos \theta) \, J_0 (\beta_0 \varrho \sin \theta) \frac{dz}{d\varrho} \right.$$

$$\left. + \cos \theta \sin (\beta_0 z \cos \theta) \, J_1 (\beta_0 \varrho \sin \theta) \right] h_A(\varrho) \, \varrho \, d\varrho \qquad (8.41)$$

An equivalent result has been verified in its application to aerials on circular plateaux and conical hills by experiments with models (Page and Monteath, 1955).

Chapter 9

A PERTURBATION METHOD BASED ON GREEN'S THEOREM

THE propagation of radio waves over non-uniform ground, which was the subject of Chapter 8, has been studied extensively in the U.S.S.R., notably by Feinberg (1944, 1945, 1946), using a perturbation method based on Green's theorem. This work was originally published during and soon after the Second World War, and for some years it tended to be overlooked. The compensation theorem method, which is very similar to the Green's theorem method, was published in ignorance of it.

The reader is referred to a review by Feinberg (1959) for references to the original papers, and to a paper by Godziński (1958) for a very clear treatment for a plane earth.

In previous chapters the boundary condition at the surface of the ground was expressed in terms of a surface impedance η. An alternative procedure is to consider the gradient $\partial E_n/\partial n$ normal to the surface of the normal component E_n of electric field. Provided that the behaviour of the surface can be represented by a surface impedance η, it can easily be shown that at the surface

$$\frac{\partial E_n}{\partial n} = \frac{j\beta_0\eta}{\eta_0}\, E_n \qquad (9.1)$$

If both η/η_0 and the slope of the surface are small the same boundary conditions may be applied with sufficient accuracy to the vertical component E_r, so that

$$\frac{\partial E_r}{\partial n} \simeq \frac{j\beta_0\eta}{\eta_0}\, E_r \qquad (9.2)$$

Note that although E_r is directed along a radius of the earth, the gradient is taken along a normal to the (generally irregular) surface. Moreover, since the radius of the earth is very large compared with the wavelength, E_r will almost exactly obey a scalar wave equation:

$$\nabla^2 E_r + \beta_0^2 E_r = \tau \tag{9.3}$$

where τ represents some distribution of sources.

Consider two distributions of sources, A and B, outside a closed surface S, and let the scalar variable E_r be ψ_A when source A operates alone and ψ_B when source B operates alone. Now Green's theorem states that

$$\iiint_v (\psi_A \nabla^2 \psi_B - \psi_B \nabla^2 \psi_A)\, dv = \iint_T \left(\psi_B \frac{\partial \psi_A}{\partial n} - \psi_A \frac{\partial \psi_B}{\partial n} \right) dS \tag{9.4}$$

where v is the volume enclosed by any closed surface T and a gradient such as $\partial \psi_A / \partial n$ is directed along the outward normal to T. (This equation does not depend on ψ_A and ψ_B satisfying the wave equation; it is sufficient that both these quantities, with their first two derivatives, should be continuous functions of position.) Now suppose that the sources A and B are volume distributions τ_A and τ_B occupying volumes v_A and v_B enclosed by two separate small surfaces S_A and S_B (Fig. 9.1) and that these are both outside a third closed surface S. S_A, S_B and S will be supposed to be enclosed in a very large sphere S_1.

Let v be the volume between S_1 and S, so that T is composed of those two surfaces. Applying eqn. (9.3), eqn. (9.4) becomes

$$\iiint_v (\psi_A \tau_B - \psi_B \tau_A)\, dv = \iint_{S_1 - S} \left(\psi_B \frac{\partial \psi_A}{\partial n} - \psi_A \frac{\partial \psi_B}{\partial n} \right) dS \tag{9.5}$$

The radiation condition, which was discussed in relation to electromagnetic fields in Chapter 2, is also applicable to a scalar satisfying the wave equation (Stratton, 1941) and it may be deduced that the surface integral over S_1 vanishes as the radius of S_1 tends to infinity. Moreover, since τ_A and τ_B are zero outside S_A and S_B respectively, the volume integral can be confined to the interiors of those surfaces.

Equation (9.5) becomes

$$\iiint_{v_B} \psi_A \tau_B \, dv - \iiint_{v_A} \psi_B \tau_A \, dv = \iint_S \left(\psi_A \frac{\partial \psi_B}{\partial n} - \psi_B \frac{\partial \psi_A}{\partial n} \right) dS$$
(9.6)

(The sign of the right-hand side has been reversed because gradients are now taken in the direction of the outward normal to S, corresponding to the inward normal to T.) If now only point sources are considered,

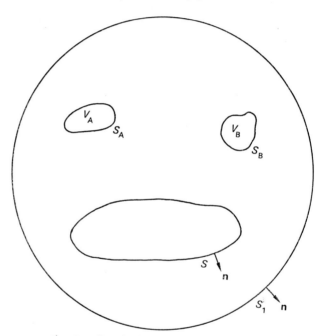

FIG. 9.1. Green's theorem perturbation formula.

S_A and S_B may be regarded as infinitesimal, so that ψ_A and ψ_B may be assigned the constant values $\psi_A(B)$ and $\psi_B(A)$ within S_B and S_A respectively, and taken outside the integrals. Equation (9.6) then becomes

$$\psi_A(B) \, U_B - \psi_B(A) \, U_A = \iint_S \left(\psi_A \frac{\partial \psi_B}{\partial n} - \psi_B \frac{\partial \psi_A}{\partial n} \right) dS \quad (9.7)$$

where

$$U_A = \iiint_{v_A} \tau_A \, dv$$

and

$$U_B = \iiint_{v_B} \tau_B \, dv$$

may be regarded as the strengths of the point sources.

The derivation of this result assumed the wave equation to be satisfied everywhere *outside* S. No assumptions were made about the interior of S, which need not be homogeneous. Moreover, the derivation is not invalidated if we assume that ψ_A results from the action of source A when one condition exists inside S and that ψ_B results from the action of source B when a totally different condition exists inside S. Using primes to indicate the latter condition, the result is

$$\psi_A(B) \, U_B - \psi'_B(A) \, U_A = \iint_S \left(\psi_A \frac{\partial \psi'_B}{\partial n} - \psi'_B \frac{\partial \psi_A}{\partial n} \right) dS \qquad (9.8)$$

For the same condition within S, making only assumptions required for reciprocity, it may be shown that

$$\psi_A(B)/U_A = \psi_B(A)/U_B$$

The result may therefore be expressed as

$$\frac{1}{U_A} [\psi'_A(B) - \psi_A(B)] = \frac{1}{U_A U_B} \iint_S \left(\psi'_B \frac{\partial \psi_A}{\partial n} - \psi_A \frac{\partial \psi'_B}{\partial n} \right) dS \qquad (9.9)$$

which is equivalent to a scalar version of eqn. (5.30), and may be used in exactly the same way as the basis of a perturbation method.

Although approximations are entailed by the use of a scalar wave equation, eqn. (9.9) often leads to precisely the same results as eqn. (5.30) after other necessary approximations have been made in each case. Godziński (1961) has in fact used the vector form of Green's theorem to derive an equation which is virtually identical to eqn. (5.30).

Since the compensation theorem and Green's theorem methods are essentially the same, leading to the same mathematical formulation of any given problem, the choice between them is a matter of personal preference. Some mathematical physicists may prefer to use Green's theorem because to them the postulation of terminals connected to aerials may seem inelegant and unnecessary. On the other hand, engineers often feel that the visualization of these concrete devices leads to a better intuitive understanding, so that the validity of approximations can be more readily assessed.

Chapter 10

RECIPROCAL AND NON-RECIPROCAL MEDIA

10.1 *Anisotropic and Optically Active Reciprocal Media*

In Chapter 2 the reciprocity principle was derived on the assumption that the medium was linear and time-independent. It was also assumed that the permittivity and permeability were scalar, but this assumption will be shown to be unnecessarily restrictive.

Suppose that we take an isotropic medium and embed in it a uniform array of parallel rods of another material having a different permittivity (Fig. 10.1). Since non-uniform media have not been

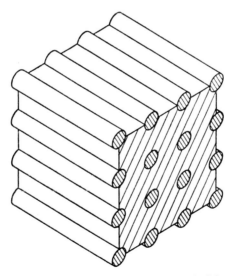

FIG. 10.1. Synthetic material equivalent to uniaxial crystal.

excluded this composite material will not invalidate reciprocity. Now suppose that both the diameter of the rods and the spacing between them are reduced until both are very small in comparison with the wavelength in either substance. The result will be an aniso-tropic medium equivalent in electrical behaviour to a uniaxial crystal, and the permittivity relating the displacement D to the electric field E will be a tensor $[\varepsilon]$. Assuming the rods to be parallel to the x-axis we have in Cartesian coordinates:

$$\begin{bmatrix} D_x \\ D_y \\ D_z \end{bmatrix} = \begin{bmatrix} \varepsilon_1 & 0 & 0 \\ 0 & \varepsilon_2 & 0 \\ 0 & 0 & \varepsilon_2 \end{bmatrix} \begin{bmatrix} E_x \\ E_y \\ E_z \end{bmatrix} \tag{10.1}$$

If a second set of rods is arranged parallel to the y-axis but differently spaced the result is equivalent to a bi-axial crystal, for which

$$\begin{bmatrix} D_x \\ D_y \\ D_z \end{bmatrix} = \begin{bmatrix} \varepsilon_{xx} & 0 & 0 \\ 0 & \varepsilon_{yy} & 0 \\ 0 & 0 & \varepsilon_{zz} \end{bmatrix} \begin{bmatrix} E_x \\ E_y \\ E_z \end{bmatrix} \tag{10.2}$$

Rotation of axes leads to the more general expression

$$\begin{bmatrix} D_x \\ D_y \\ D_z \end{bmatrix} = \begin{bmatrix} \varepsilon_{xx} & \varepsilon_{xy} & \varepsilon_{xz} \\ \varepsilon_{yx} & \varepsilon_{yy} & \varepsilon_{yz} \\ \varepsilon_{zx} & \varepsilon_{zy} & \varepsilon_{zz} \end{bmatrix} \begin{bmatrix} E_x \\ E_y \\ E_z \end{bmatrix} \tag{10.3}$$

in which the tensor $[\varepsilon]$ is symmetrical about the main diagonal, so that

$$\left. \begin{aligned} \varepsilon_{xy} &= \varepsilon_{yx} \\ \varepsilon_{yz} &= \varepsilon_{zy} \\ \varepsilon_{zx} &= \varepsilon_{xz} \end{aligned} \right\} \tag{10.4}$$

In the same way, by postulating an array of rods of magnetic material, it is easy to show that the permeability also may be generalized to a symmetric tensor without invalidating reciprocity.

It is not in fact necessary to assume that the material can be completely described in terms of permeability and permittivity tensors. Suppose that a uniform isotropic medium has embedded in it randomly arranged short conducting helices—all right-handed. If these are sufficiently small in relation to the wavelength and sufficiently numerous the material will appear uniform and isotropic, since in the bulk material all directions must be equivalent. Assuming the matrix material to be a lossless dielectric and the helices to be perfect conductors those helices whose axes are not perpendicular to E will carry circulating currents proportional to $j\omega E$. They will therefore act as magnetic dipoles and contribute to the fields a component of magnetic induction proportional to $j\omega E$, since on the average components of induction perpendicular to E will cancel one another.

If, on the other hand, the composite material is subjected to an alternating magnetic field H, e.m.f.s proportional to $j\omega H$ will be induced in them and they will then become electrically polarized, contributing to the fields a component of electric displacement proportional to $-j\omega H$.

To sum up, the electric displacement and magnetic induction are related to the electric and magnetic fields by equations of the form

$$\left.\begin{aligned} B &= \mu H + j\omega k_1 E \\ D &= \varepsilon E - j\omega k_2 H \end{aligned}\right\} \tag{10.5}$$

and it may be shown that

$$k_1 = k_2 = k \tag{10.6}$$

By postulating helices arranged parallel to one or two axes these equations may be generalized to describe anisotropic media for which μ, ε, and k are all tensors. Such a medium can still obey the reciprocity principle.

Materials characterized by eqns. (10.5) and (10.6) are, in the language of physical chemistry, *optically active*. Solutions of substances, such as many compounds produced by biological processes, whose molecules would appear changed by reflection in a mirror, possess this property. They rotate the plane of polarization of electromagnetic waves passing through them, but this rotation does not imply any violation of reciprocity because it is always clockwise (or anti-clockwise) with respect to the direction of propagation. If plane-polarized plane waves are reflected back along their original path the polarization is rotated back into its original direction.

10.2 Non-reciprocal Media

The first general treatment of non-reciprocal media was published by D. H. Tellegen (1948) who postulated a medium obeying the following generalization of two of Maxwell's equations:

$$B = [\mu] H + [k_B] E \tag{10.7}$$

$$D = [k_D] H + [\varepsilon] E \tag{10.8}$$

$[\mu]$ and $[\varepsilon]$ are the permeability and permittivity tensors, expressed (using rationalized m.k.s. units) in henrys per metre and farads per metre respectively. The tensors $[k_B]$ and $[k_D]$, which are zero in ordinary isotropic or anisotropic media (but equal and opposite in optically active reciprocal media), are expressed in seconds per metre.

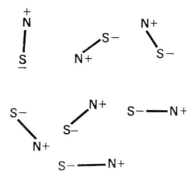

FIG. 10.2. Magneto-electric medium.

Tellegen pointed out that a non-reciprocal medium in which $[k_B]$ and $[k_D]$ are not zero could be formed by dispersing in an ordinary medium particles having both a magnetic moment and an electric dipole moment, as shown in Fig. 10.2, a North magnetic pole always being associated with the same sign of charge. Suppose that these particles have some freedom to rotate in response to an applied electric or magnetic field. If they are randomly oriented in an isotropic matrix, $[k_B]$ and $[k_D]$, like $[\mu]$ and $[\varepsilon]$, are scalar, but in a crystal all four quantities may be tensors. The medium differs from an optically active reciprocal medium in that $[k_B]$ and $[k_D]$ may be shown to be equal, instead of equal and opposite. Such media (O'Dell, 1965) do not exist in nature because there is no reason why a North pole should be associated with a charge of one sign rather than the other. They can, however, be produced artificially by applying parallel electric and magnetic fields to certain substances, such as chromium oxide, while they are cooled to a temperature at which the electric and magnetic polarizations become permanent (Dzyaloshinskii, 1960).

Suppose that eqns. (2.3) and (2.4) are replaced by eqns. (10.7) and (10.8). Instead of eqn. (2.7) we find

$$\mathrm{div}\,(E_1 \times H_2 - E_2 \times H_1) = -E_1 . J_2 + E_2 . J_1 + H_1 . M_2 - H_2 . M_1$$

$$-j\omega\,\{E_1 . ([\varepsilon]\,E_2) - E_2 . ([\varepsilon]\,E_1)$$

$$- H_1 . ([\mu]\,H_2) + H_2 . ([\mu]\,H_1)$$

$$+ E_1 . ([k_D]\,H_2) + H_2 . ([k_B]\,E_1)$$

$$- H_1 . ([k_B]\,E_2) - E_2 . ([k_D]\,H_1)\}$$

$$(10.9)$$

The reciprocity principle is satisfied if eqn. (2.7) is satisfied; this requires the quantity multiplying $j\omega$ in eqn. (10.9) to be zero for all values of E_1, E_2, H_1 and H_2. The following four equations must therefore all be satisfied:

$$E_1 . ([\varepsilon]\,E_2) = E_2 . ([\varepsilon]\,E_1) \qquad (10.10)$$

$$H_1 . ([\mu]\,H_2) = H_2 . ([\mu]\,H_1) \qquad (10.11)$$

$$E_1 . ([k_D]\,H_2) = -H_2 . ([k_B]\,E_1) \qquad (10.12)$$

$$H_1 . ([k_B]\,E_2) = -E_2 . ([k_D]\,H_1) \qquad (10.13)$$

If the vectors and tensors are expressed in Cartesian form as in eqn. (10.3) and the multiplications are performed, the conditions for reciprocity are found to be

$$\varepsilon_{xy} = \varepsilon_{yx} \quad \text{etc.} \tag{10.14}$$

$$\mu_{xy} = \mu_{yx} \quad \text{etc.} \tag{10.15}$$

$$k_{Bxx} = -k_{Dxx} \quad \text{etc.} \tag{10.16}$$

$$k_{Bxy} = -k_{Dyx} \quad \text{etc.} \tag{10.17}$$

These equations may be condensed to

$$[\varepsilon] = [\varepsilon]' \tag{10.18}$$

$$[\mu] = [\mu]' \tag{10.19}$$

$$[k_B] = -[k_D]' \tag{10.20}$$

where the prime indicates matrix transposition. For an isotropic medium eqns. (10.18) and (10.19) are trivial, but eqn. (10.20) becomes

$$k_B + k_D = 0 \tag{10.21}$$

Provided that the medium satisfies eqns. (10.18)–(10.20) the fundamental statements of the reciprocity principle contained in eqns. (2.9)–(2.11) are valid, as are the derived results: network theorems, Huygens' principle and perturbation formulae. The volume integral perturbation formula (eqn. (15.11)) would of course require generalization if the change under investigation were not merely a change of scalar permittivity and permeability.

There are three basic classes of non-reciprocal media, each violating one of the three equations (10.18), (10.19) and (10.20), but a medium may fall into more than one class. Media violating eqn. (10.18) or eqn. (10.19) are necessarily anisotropic, but a medium violating eqn. (10.20) may be isotropic.

Media violating eqn. (10.20), termed magneto-electric media, have already been discussed. Tellegen (1948) showed that such a medium could be used to form an antireciprocal fourpole circuit element (i.e.

one in which the mutual impedances Z_{AB} and Z_{BA} are equal and opposite) which he termed a *gyrator*. Figure 10.3 shows the simplest arrangement in which a cylinder of such a material acts both as the core of a coil and the dielectric of a capacitor. No material is known to exhibit a magneto-electric effect of sufficient magnitude to produce a useful device of any kind.

Of the other two types of medium the best known is an ionized gas, such as that constituting the ionosphere, in the presence of a steady

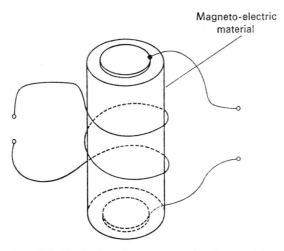

Magneto-electric
material

FIG. 10.3. Gyrator based on magneto-electric material.

magnetic field (Kelso, 1964). For example, if this field is directed along the z-axis and an alternating electric field is applied along either the x-axis or the y-axis free electrons will move in elliptical orbits in the xy plane so that there are components of electric polarization in both the x and y directions (Fig. 10.4). ε_{xy} and ε_{yx} are found to be of equal magnitude but opposite sign. (In the absence of dissipation they are both imaginary.) The propagation of plane waves parallel to the z-axis is best studied by resolving them into two components circularly polarized in opposite directions. These have different phase velocities, so that the plane of polarization of plane-polarized waves is rotated as in an optically active medium. The direction of rotation is, however, that of a right-handed screw when propagation is in the positive *H* direction but that of a left-handed screw when propagation is in the negative *H* direction. If a plane-polarized wave is reflected back along

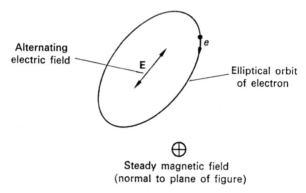

Fig. 10.4. Motion of electron in the presence of a steady magnetic field.

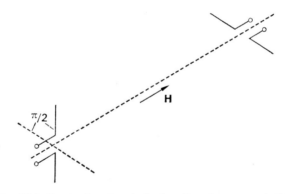

Fig. 10.5. Gyrator based on ionized medium in a magnetic field.

its path the rotation of the plane of polarization rotates onwards—not back to its original direction as in an optically active but reciprocal medium—so that reciprocity is violated. For example, if two orthogonal dipoles are arranged as in Fig. 10.5 the fourpole so formed is anti-reciprocal.

Analogous but magnetic phenomena occur in magnetic materials, particularly ferrites and garnets, in the presence of a steady magnetic field. The magnetic moment of an unpaired electron is associated with angular momentum so that the axis of spin precesses about the magnetic field when this is first applied, but the dissipation of energy causes the precession to be damped out until the axis of spin is aligned with the field. If now an alternating field is applied perpendicularly to the steady field, precession will again be induced, and there will result components of magnetic induction both parallel to and perpendicular to the applied field. If the steady field is applied along the z-axis, the permeability tensor takes the form

$$\begin{bmatrix} \mu_1 & -j\varkappa & 0 \\ j\varkappa & \mu_1 & 0 \\ 0 & 0 & \mu_2 \end{bmatrix}$$

In the absence of dissipation μ_1, μ_2 and $\varkappa$ are all real, but dissipation results in imaginary components.

Plane-polarized plane waves traversing a gyromagnetic medium along the magnetic field may be resolved into two circularly polarized components, one rotating in the same direction as in the precession and the other in the opposite direction. The effective permeabilities for the two components will be different, and these components will be propagated with different velocities and will be attenuated differently. The difference between the phase velocities causes the plane of polarization of the original linearly polarized wave to rotate.

Clarricoats (1961) gives a useful treatment of the physics of gyromagnetic media and describes microwave devices exploiting their non-reciprocal properties.

The three basic types of non-reciprocal medium (violating eqns. (10.18), (10.19) and (10.20) respectively) are not entirely independent, since it is possible to conceive (quite impractically) the formation of any one of them by embedding small devices using any of the others in a reciprocal medium. For example, Fig. 10.6 shows a ferrite toroid which is subjected to a radial magnetic field by means of an inner permanently magnetized toroid. Suppose that such a device could be made extremely small, and that a large number of them, all with the North poles on the outside, are dispersed at random in a reciprocal medium. Considering one ferrite toroid and taking cylindrical polar coordinates as shown, the permeability tensor will be such that

$$\mu_{z\phi} = -\mu_{\phi z} \neq 0$$

An alternating magnetic field in the z-direction will therefore result in a component of magnetic induction in the ϕ-direction and this will

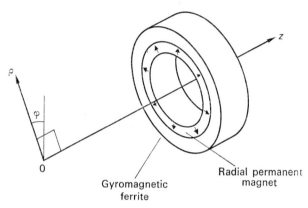

FIG. 10.6. Use of a gyromagnetic substance to produce a magneto-electric medium.

induce an electric polarization parallel to the z-axis. On the other hand, an alternating electric field in the z-direction will result in a magnetic field in the ϕ-direction, and this in turn will produce a magnetic moment in the z-direction. The signs of these effects are such that the presence of a large number of the toroids randomly oriented will result in an isotropic medium violating eqn. (10.20) (or 10.21) in that $k_B = k_D \neq 0$. It would, however, appear impracticable to produce a non-reciprocal effect of useful magnitude in this way.

The foregoing discussion provides a basis for answering the question: "Why is the reciprocity principle so widely applicable without being universally true?"

Reciprocity failure requires asymmetry of a type that enables one type of magnetic pole—say the North—to be associated with one sign of electric charge, positive or negative. Now since we live in a world of matter, rather than anti-matter, positive and negative charges are distinguished, in that the lighter particles are negative. Once a steady magnetic field exists, then one sign of magnetic pole may be associated with each direction, with the field or against it. It is this singling out of one sign of pole and one sign of charge that leads to reciprocity failure. No corresponding effect will be associated with a steady electric field, since symmetry exists between the two signs of magnetic pole; non-reciprocal media existing in nature are always permeated by a steady magnetic field.

Magneto-electric media, which can exhibit reciprocity failure even in the absence of a steady magnetic field, require human ingenuity for their creation. For example, in the aggregate of magnetized toroids discussed above, all must be magnetized in the same direction, so that a distinction between North and South poles is created.

REFERENCES

ANDERSEN, J.B. (1963) The radiation field from a vertical dipole over inhomogeneous ground, in *Electromagnetic Theory and Antennas* (ed. Jordan, E.C.) Part 2, p. 1099, Pergamon Press, Oxford.

ANDERSEN, J.B. (1967) An analysis of surface wave antennas, in *Electromagnetic Theory—Proceedings of a Symposium held at Delft, The Netherlands, Sept.* 1965, p. 729, Pergamon Press, Oxford.

BAKER, B.B., and COPSON, E.T. (1953) *The Mathematical Theory of Huygens' Principle*, Oxford University Press, 2nd ed.

BALLANTINE, S. (1928) The Lorentz reciprocity principle for electromagnetic waves, *Proc. Inst. Radio Engrs* 16, 513.

BALLANTINE, S. (1929) Reciprocity in electromagnetic, mechanical, acoustical, and interconnected systems, *Proc. Inst. Radio Engrs* 17, 929.

BAÑOS, A. (1966) *Dipole Radiation in the Presence of a Conducting Half-space*, Pergamon Press, Oxford.

BOOKER, H.G. (1946) Slot aerials and their relation to complementary wire aerials (Babinet's principle), *J. Instn elect. Engrs* 93 (IIIA), 620.

BOOKER, H.G., and GORDON, W.E. (1950) A theory of radio scattering in the troposphere, *Proc. Inst. Radio Engrs* 38, 401.

BREMMER, H. (1949) *Terrestrial Radio Waves*, Elsevier, Amsterdam.

BROWN, G.H. (1935) The phase and magnitude of earth currents near radio transmitting antennas, *Proc. Inst. Radio Engrs* 23, 168.

BROWN, J. (1958) A generalised form of the reciprocity theorem, *Proc. Instn. elect. Engrs* 105C, 472.

CARTER, P.S. (1932) Circuit relations in radiating systems and applications to antenna problems, *Proc. Inst. Radio Engrs* 20, 1004.

CHRISTIANSEN, S., and LARSEN, T. (1967) Numerical application of the compensation theorem to mixed-path propagation problems, *Radio Sci.* 2, 1471.

CLARRICOATS, P.J.P. (1961) *Microwave Ferrites*, Chapman & Hall, London.

CLEMMOW, P.C. (1966) *The Plane Wave Spectrum Representation of Electromagnetic Waves*, Pergamon Press, Oxford.

CULLEN, A.L., and PARR, J.C. (1955) A new perturbation method for measuring microwave fields in free space, *Proc. Instn. elect. Engrs* 102B, 836.

DZYALOSHINSKII, I.E. (1960) On the magneto-electrical effect in antiferromagnets, *Soviet Phys. JETP* 37, 628.

FEINBERG, E.L. (1944) On the propagation of radio waves along an imperfect surface, Parts 1 and 2, *Jour. Phys. USSR* 8, 317.

FEINBERG, E.L. (1945) On the propagation of radio waves along an imperfect surface, Part 3, *Jour. Phys. USSR* 9, 1.

FEINBERG, E.L. (1946) On the propagation of radio waves along an imperfect surface, Part 4, *J. Phys. USSR* **10**, 410.

FEINBERG, E.L. (1959) Propagation of radio waves along an inhomogeneous surface, *Nuovo Cimento* **11**, 60.

GODZIŃSKI, Z. (1958) The use of equivalent secondary sources in the theory of groundwave propagation over an inhomogeneous earth, *Proc. Instn. elect. Engrs* **105C**, 448.

GODZIŃSKI, Z. (1961) The surface impedance concept and the structure of radio waves over real earth, *Proc. Instn. elect. Engrs* **108C**, 362.

HUFFORD, G.A. (1952) An integral equation approach to the problem of wave propagation over an irregular surface, *Q. appl. Math.* **9**, 391.

JORDAN, E.C., and BALMAIN, K.G. (1968) *Electromagnetic Waves and Radiating Systems*, Prentice-Hall, New York, 2nd ed.

KELSO, J.M. (1964) *Radio Ray Propagation in the Ionosphere*, McGraw-Hill, New York.

KING, R.J. (1965) An amplitude and phase measuring system using a small modulated scatterer, *Microwave J.* **8**, 51.

KING, R.J. (1969) Electromagnetic wave propagation over a constant impedance plane, *Radio Sci.* **4**, 255.

KING, R.J., and MALEY, S.W. (1965) Model experiments on propagation of groundwaves across an abrupt boundary at perpendicular incidence, *J. Res. natn. Bur. Stand.* **69D**, 1375.

KING, R.J. and MALEY, S.W. (1966) Model experiments on propagation of groundwaves across an abrupt boundary at oblique incidence, *Radio Sci.* **1**, 111.

KING, R.J., MALEY, S.W., and WAIT, J.R. (1966) Groundwave propagation along three-section mixed paths, *Proc. Instn. elect. Engrs* **113**, 747.

LORENTZ, H.A. (1895) Vorslagen van de gewone vergadering der wis- en natuurkundige afdeeling, *Proc. K. Ned. Akad. Wet.* **4**, 176.

MALEY, S.W., and OTTESEN, H. (1964) An experimental study of mixed path ground wave propagation, *J. Res. natn. Bur. Stand.* **68D**, 915.

MILLAR, R.F. (1967) Propagation of electromagnetic waves near a coastline on a flat earth, *Radio Sci.* **2**, 261.

MILLINGTON, G. (1949) Groundwave propagation over an inhomogeneous smooth earth, *Proc. Instn. elect. Engrs* **96**, Part III, 53.

MONTEATH, G.D. (1951) Application of the compensation theorem to certain radiation and propagation problems, *Proc. Instn. elect. Engrs* **98**, Part IV, 23.

MONTEATH, G.D. (1958) The effect of the ground constants, and of an earth system, on the performance of a vertical medium-wave aerial, *Proc. Instn. elect. Engrs* **105**, Part IV, 292.

MONTEATH, G.D. (1959) Reciprocity in radio-frequency measurements, *Electron. Radio Engr* **36**, 18.

NORTON, K.A. (1936) The propagation of radio waves over the surface of the earth and in the upper atmosphere. Part I—Groundwave propagation from short antennas, *Proc. Inst. Radio Engrs* **24**, 1367.

NORTON, K.A. (1937) The propagation of radio waves over the surface of the earth and in the upper atmosphere. Part II—The propagation from vertical, horizontal and loop antennas over a plane earth of finite conductivity, *Proc. Inst. Radio Engrs* **25**, 1203.

NORTON, K.A. (1941) The calculation of groundwave field intensity over a finitely conducting spherical earth, *Proc. Inst. Radio Engrs* **29**, 623.

O'DELL, T.H. (1965) Magnetoelectrics—a new class of materials, *Electronics and Power* **11**, 266.

OTT, R.H., and BERRY, L.A. (1970) An alternative integral equation for propagation over irregular terrain, *Radio Sci.* **5**, 767.

PAGE, H., and MONTEATH, G.D. (1955) The vertical radiation patterns of medium-wave broadcasting aerials, *Proc. Instn. elect. Engrs* **102B**, 279.

PISTOLKORS, A.A. (1929) The radiation resistance of beam antennas, *Proc. Inst. Radio Engrs* **17**, 562.

RAYLEIGH, LORD (1894) *Theory of Sound*, Macmillan, London, 2nd ed., p. 155.

ROBIEUX, J. (1957) Interaction entre deux aériens, *C.R. Acad. Sci. (Paris)* **245**, 793.

ROBIEUX, J. (1959) Lois générales de la liaison entre radiateurs d'ondes. Applications aux ondes de surface et à la propagation, *Annls Radioélect.* **14**, 187.

RUMSEY, V.H. (1954) Reaction concept in electromagnetic theory, *Phys. Rev.* **94**, 1483.

SCHELKUNOFF, S.A. (1938) The impedance concept and its application to problems of reflection, refraction, shielding and power absorption, *Bell Syst. tech. J.* **17**, 17.

SOMMERFELD, A., and RENNER, F. (1942) Radiation energy and earth absorption for dipole antennae, *Wireless Engr* **19**, 351, 409, 457.

STRATTON, J.A. (1941) *Electromagnetic Theory*, McGraw-Hill, New York, p. 485.

TELLEGEN, B.D.H. (1948) The gyrator, a new electric network element, *Philips Res. Rep.* **3**, 81. ·

WAIT, J.R. (1954) Theory of electromagnetic waves over geological conductors, *Geofis. pura appl.* **28**, 47.

WAIT, J.R. (1956a) Effect of the ground screen on the field radiated from a monopole, *I.R.E. Trans.* **AP-4**, 179.

WAIT, J.R. (1956b) Mixed-path groundwave propagation—1 Short distances, *J. Res. natn. Bur. Stand.* **57**, 1.

WAIT, J.R. (1957a) The impedance of a wire grid parallel to a dielectric interface, *I.R.E. Trans.* **MTT-5**, 99.

WAIT, J.R. (1957b) Amplitude and phase of the low-frequency groundwave near a coast line, *J. Res. natn. Bur. Stand.* **58**, 237.

WAIT, J.R. (1958a) On the theory of propagation of electromagnetic waves along a curved surface, *Can. J. Phys.* **36**, 9.

WAIT, J.R. (1958b) On the calculation of transverse current loss in buried-wire ground systems, *Appl. scient. Res.* **B7**, 81.

WAIT, J.R. (1961) On the theory of mixed-path groundwave propagation on a spherical earth, *J. Res. natn. Bur. Stand.* **65D**, 401.

WAIT, J.R. (1962) Propagation of electromagnetic waves along the earth's surface, in *Electromagnetic Waves* (ed. Langer, R.E.), University Press, Wisconsin.

WAIT, J.R. (1963a) The theory of an antenna over an inhomogeneous ground plane, in *Electromagnetic Theory and Antennas* (ed. Jordan, E.C.), Pergamon Press, Oxford.

WAIT, J.R. (1963b) Oblique propagation of groundwaves across a coastline—Part I, *J. Res. natn. Bur. Stand.* **67D**, 617.

WAIT, J.R. (1964a) Electromagnetic surface waves, in *Advances in Radio Research* (ed. Saxton, J.A.), Academic Press, London.

WAIT, J.R. (1964b) Oblique propagation of groundwaves across a coastline—Part III, *Radio Sci.* **68D**, 291.

WAIT, J.R. (1967) Pattern of a linear antenna erected over a tapered ground screen, *Can. J. Phys.* **45**, 3091.

WAIT, J.R. (1969) Impedance characteristics of electric dipoles over a conducting half-space, *Radio Sci.* **4**, 971.

WAIT, J.R., and HOUSEHOLDER, J. (1957) Mixed-path groundwave propagation—2 Larger distances, *J. Res. natn. Bur. Stand.* **59**, 19.

WAIT, J.R., and JACKSON, C.M. (1963) Oblique propagation of groundwaves across a coastline—Part II, *J. Res. natn. Bur. Stand.* **67D**, 625.

WAIT, J.R., and POPE, W.A. (1954) The characteristics of a vertical antenna with a radial conductor ground system, *Appl. scient. Res.* **B4**, 177.

WAIT, J.R., and POPE, W.A. (1955) Input resistance of l.f. unipole aerials, *Wireless Engr* **32**, 131.

WAIT, J.R., and SPIES, K.P. (1964) Propagation of radio waves past a coastline with a gradual change of surface impedance, *I.E.E.E. Trans.* **AP-12**, 570.

WAIT, J.R., and SPIES, K.P. (1970) Integral equation approach to the radiation from a vertical antenna over an inhomogeneous ground plane, *Radio Sci.* **5**, 73.

WAIT, J.R., and SURTEES, W.J. (1954) Impedance of a top-loaded antenna of arbitrary length over a circular grounded screen, *J. appl. Phys.* **25**, 553.

WAIT, J.R., and WALTERS, L.C. (1963) Curves for groundwave propagation over mixed land and sea paths, *I.E.E.E. Trans.* **AP-11**, 38.

NAME INDEX

143

SUBJECT INDEX

145